LECTURES ON THE KIDNEY

LECTURES ON THE KIDNEY

BY

HOMER W. SMITH, A.B., Sc.D., M.S.

Professor of Physiology and Chairman of the Physiology Laboratories,
New York University College of Medicine, New York

PORTER LECTURES—SERIES IX

Delivered at the
University of Kansas School of Medicine
Lawrence, Kansas City

THE WILLIAM HENRY WELCH LECTURES

Delivered at the
Mount Sinai Hospital
New York City

Published by the
UNIVERSITY EXTENSION DIVISION
UNIVERSITY OF KANSAS
LAWRENCE, KANSAS

Copyright, 1943, by

UNIVERSITY EXTENSION DIVISION
UNIVERSITY OF KANSAS
LAWRENCE, KANSAS

Printed in the United States of America by
WAVERLY PRESS, INC.,
Baltimore, Maryland.

Reprint by
JOHN S. SWIFT CO., INC.
Operating Plants in
Chicago - St. Louis - New York - Cincinnati

In 1918, Dr. J. L. Porter, a general practitioner of Paola, Kansas, bequeathed all of his property to the School of Medicine of the University of Kansas, providing for a scholarship and permitting the authorities to use the balance of the income for any purpose they deemed best.

It was decided to use this fund to defray the expenses of a series of lectures to be given by outstanding members of the medical profession. The first of these was delivered in April, 1930, by Dr. L. F. Barker; the second was given in October, 1930, by Dr. Joseph Collins; the third was given in March, 1933, by Dr. J. S. Horsley; the fourth in 1934, by Dr. Richard Scammon; the fifth by Dr. Edward A. Doisy, in 1935; the sixth by Dr. Jennings C. Litzenberg, in 1936; the seventh by Dr. Chevalier Jackson, in 1937; the eighth by Dr. William Boyd, in 1938; and the ninth series, delivered in 1939, follows.

The William Henry Welch Lectures were founded in 1926 by Dr. Emanual Libman for the purpose of bringing to The Mount Sinai Hospital distinguished men of medical science who would present the results of their investigations.

The lectures are delivered annually or biannually and in selecting topics and lecturers emphasis is laid upon the demonstration of new concepts and new methods in medicine and surgery.

The following lectures have been presented to date: 1927, Prof. Richard Willstätter; 1929, Dr. Simon Flexner; 1930, Dr. Theobald Smith; 1931, Dr. Harvey Cushing; 1934, Prof. James B. Collip; 1935, Dr. George Hoyt Whipple; 1937, Sir Henry H. Dale; 1938, Prof. Walter Bradford Cannon; 1939, Dr. Herbert M. Evans; 1940, Dr. Peyton Rous; 1943, Dr. Homer W. Smith.

FOREWORD

The clinical studies reported here have been conducted as a collaborative program of the Department of Medicine and the Department of Physiology of New York University College of Medicine. All the work presented in the last lecture and much of that abstracted from earlier studies has been made possible by the aid of the Commonwealth Fund.

The author is indebted [to Dr. William Goldring, Dr. Herbert Chasis, Dr. Hilmert A. Ranges and Dr. Stanley Bradley, for permission to include published and unpublished data.

TABLE OF CONTENTS

* Porter Lecture
** William Henry Welch Lecture

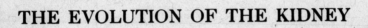

THE EVOLUTION OF THE KIDNEY

THE EVOLUTION OF THE KIDNEY*

Seventy-odd years have elapsed since Claude Bernard first apprehended the fact that the true medium in which we live is neither air nor water, but the blood, the internal medium, that bathes our muscles, glands and brain. This internal environment, as he called it, is a cosmos elaborately isolated from the external world and protected by a variety of physiological devices to the end that its composition shall remain unaffected by the sudden and sometimes severe changes that beset the other and unstable cosmos that lies outside our skins.

During the seven decades since Bernard formulated this concept, there has been discovered feature after feature in our *milieu intérieur* to which his concept of physiological regulation must be applied. Vital phenomena involve the interplay of so many physical-chemical factors that only a beginning can be made towards enumerating them. The most important one is, of course, water itself, the chief constituent of the blood and tissues; then there are the numerous inorganic salts: sodium, potassium, magnesium, calcium, chloride, phosphate and bicarbonate, the delicate and precisely balanced acid and basic components, glucose and amino acids. This list, though incomplete, is long enough to emphasize the biological importance of the mixture as a whole. The lungs serve to maintain the composition of the blood with respect to oxygen and carbon dioxide, and with this their duty ends. The responsibility for maintaining the composition of the blood in respect to other constituents devolves largely upon the kidneys. It is no exaggeration to say that the composition of the blood is determined not by what the mouth ingests but by what the kidneys keep; they are the master chemists of our internal environment, which, so to speak, they synthesize in reverse. When, among other duties, they excrete the ashes of our body fires, or remove from the blood the infinite variety of foreign substances which are constantly being absorbed from our indiscriminate gastro-intestinal tracts, these excretory operations are incidental to the major task of keeping our internal environment in an ideal, balanced state. Our glands, our muscles, our bones, our tendons, even our brains, are called upon to do only one kind of physiological work, while our kidneys are called upon to perform an innumerable variety of operations. Bones can break, muscles can atrophy, glands can loaf, even the brain can go to sleep, without immediately endangering our survival, but when the kidneys fail to manufacture the proper kind of blood neither bone, muscle, gland nor brain can carry on. To quote Bernard again, 'In proportion as we ascend the scale of living beings, the organism grows more complex, the organic units become more delicate and require a more perfected internal environment'. It was the view of this physiologist that we achieve a free and independent life, mentally and physically, because of the constancy of the composition of our blood. Recognizing that we have the kind of blood

* This lecture is based in part on investigations cited in the bibliography, and in part upon unpublished studies of the fish kidney. A large part of the material upon which these studies are based was collected in 1930 while the author was a Fellow of the John Simon Guggenheim Memorial Foundation.

3

we have because we have the kind of kidneys that we have, we must acknowledge that our kidneys constitute the major foundation of our physiological freedom. Superficially, it might be said that the function of the kidneys is to make urine; but in a more considered view one can say that the kidneys make the stuff of philosophy itself.

Taken as a whole, the human kidney appears to be extraordinarily complex, but on anatomical analysis this complexity is reducible to fairly simple terms. Each of the two kidneys, which are of about the same size, is made up of slightly more than one million microscopic units, or nephrons. (See Figure 1 of the following lecture.) These nephrons are all essentially alike and consist of a filtering bed composed of a capillary tuft, or glomerulus, which drains directly into a long, elaborate tubule. These million-odd glomerular-tubular units empty into common collecting ducts which through confluent union finally deliver the urine into the pelvis of the kidney, whence it flows down the ureter into the bladder. In the two million-odd glomeruli, i.e., in the renal filtering bed where the formation of urine begins, the blood is literally spread out over a great surface by being divided among the innumerable capillary channels. The total surface of the glomerular capillary bed in the two human kidneys exceeds 1.0 sq. meter. Through this bed there are filtered off in each minute's time about 125 cc. of water, or about 0.01 cc. per square centimeter per minute, which is a rate of filtration well below that of the ordinary laboratory filters. But this capillary bed is still a filter in the ordinary laboratory sense for it permits everything in the plasma to pass through it except the blood cells, the plasma proteins and similar large molecular aggregates. To supply this 125 cc. of filtrate 1200 cc. of blood are perfused each minute through the capillary bed of the glomeruli.

After leaving the glomerulus the blood passes into a second set of capillaries surrounding the tubule; here an opportunity is afforded for the tubule cells to transfer various substances from blood to tubular urine, or from tubular urine back into the blood, and here is where all specific chemical operations are carried out. For as the glomerular filtrate passes down the tubules valuable substances such as glucose, sodium, chloride, amino acids, etc., are reabsorbed and returned to the blood by various processes of tubular reabsorption. At the same time certain waste products and foreign substances are taken from the blood by the tubule cells and transferred to the tubular urine. These excreted substances and such waste products and foreign compounds as are present in the original filtrate but are themselves not reabsorbed, remain in the tubular fluid to be excreted in the urine. Of all substances reabsorbed by the tubules water is reabsorbed to the greatest extent: out of the 125 cc. of filtrate formed each minute, on the average 124 cc. of water are reabsorbed, leaving only 1.0 cc. to be excreted as urine. In consequence of this extensive reabsorption of water, such substances as are filtered through the glomeruli but are themselves not reabsorbed by the tubules appear in the final urine in a highly concentrated form.[34]

In requiring how the renal tubule elaborates the glomerular filtrate into urine it will be noted that this tubule is cytologically differentiated into three segments:

a proximal segment, an intermediate thin segment, and a distal segment with drains into an arborized system of collecting tubules. The proximal segment appears to be a jack-of-all-trades, capable of reabsorbing valuable constituents, notably glucose and chloride, from the glomerular filtrate, and at the same time capable of transporting many waste products and foreign substances from blood to urine. On rather indirect evidence it has been inferred that the thin segment is responsible for the final reabsorption of water and the production of a highly concentrated urine. The function of the distal segment remains something of a mystery, but there are reasons to believe that it is responsible for the adjustment of the acidity of the urine, for the conservation of the alkali reserve of the blood, and perhaps for the chemical formation of ammonia. In the present stage of our knowledge it would be dangerous to be dogmatic about details, and in any case it is not my intention to discuss the finer points of renal function. We are concerned here only with the general pattern of structure and function in this nephric unit, and with the inquiry, How did our kidney come to have the architecture that it does? In pursuit of this inquiry we must digress from the structure of the kidney to the general evolutionary history of the vertebrates, which history must itself be prefaced by a brief discussion of the structure of the earth.

According to the geologist the continents upon which we live are but irregular slabs of granite some 15 to 40 miles thick, floating like isolated islands upon a bed of basalt, the rock which makes up the oceanic floor. Under this bed of basalt, which is only some 700 miles thick, is a zone of semi-fluid magma extending to a total depth of about 1800 miles. Innermost is a core of iron, some 4000 miles in diameter, which is raised far above incandescent heat (6,000°C.) by the enormous pressure existing at the center of the earth. It is now generally agreed by the geologist and the astronomer that the earth was separated from the sun about 2000 million years ago through disruption of the parent body by a passing star, but the daughter planet remained molten and homogeneous for only a short time, quickly acquiring its present stratified structure as it cooled and crystallized.

The continents float above the average level of the earth's crust because their granite is lighter than the basaltic bed upon which they rest; as their exposed masses weather down and the silt is deposited in the sea along their edges, the added weight of this deposit causes the plastic basalt to flow beneath the land masses and to float them higher in the air. It is these slow adjustments to maintain isostatic equilibrium between the continents and the oceanic floor that sometimes cause abrupt movements of the land.[6, 20] But all the earthquakes of historic time are trivial when compared with the disturbances of the past, which have extended not over days or weeks, but millions of years.

As measured, quite accurately it is now believed, by the radio-active clock within its rocks, the earth has had its present cold and semi-solid form for about 1800 million years. During this period it has been cooling and shrinking as a whole, having decreased in diameter something between 200 and 400 miles. Under the stresses resulting from this cooling process, and more particularly in consequence of the alternate fusion and solidification of the basaltic crust, this shrinking has been intermittent rather than uniform, so that at recurrent intervals of roughly 30 million years the continental masses have been wrinkled and folded into great mountain chains. During the intervening periods of geologic quiescence, the mountains raised by the preceding diastrophic movement have been largely if not entirely worn away to sea level by the slow erosion of wind and rain. Schuchert[29] estimates that the total continental depth eroded in this manner since the opening of the Paleozoic exceeds 75 vertical miles, or more than twenty ranges of mountains like the present European Alps or the American Rockies.

These periodic revolutions, as the geologist calls them, have made us what we are. Because they have changed the form and size of the continents and seas and at times submerged great areas of land beneath the water, because they have diverted oceanic currents, altered the dust and water vapor in the atmosphere, raised barriers to moisture-laden winds and otherwise interfered with the basal forces that control the weather, these revolutions have been accompanied by marked and protracted changes in climate over the entire surface of the earth. In general, periods of mountain building have been accompanied by marked refrigeration so that in some instances glaciers have descended to sea level in equatorial latitudes; while in the quiescent intervals, after erosion had levelled the recently formed mountains to mere hills, warm shallow seas have transgressed widely over the low-lying lands, and even Arctica and Antarctica have enjoyed a climate that was warm and humid.[28]

According to modern experimental biology, the *vis a tergo* of evolution is the production of new varieties in consequence of random mutations in the chromosomes; such of these varieties as are unfitted to survive are pruned away by natural selection, leaving the better fitted mutants to get along as best they can. Mutation is fundamental to evolution, but mutation itself would be of little avail to modify organic pattern did not the *vis a fronte* of natural selection foster the survival of exotic individuals, of the new mutations, by offering them a special environment in which their unique characters are advantageous, by preserving them from genetic extinction through backbreeding with the unmutated forms, and probably in other ways. We may believe that in the shaping of the final evolutionary product as we see it now, mutation and environment have played balanced and equal roles. Though we cannot assign to either mutation or selection any teleological direction, they tend within certain limits to have one result: after a few million years, when many millions of mutations have occurred and most of them have become extinct, we can expect to find among the surviving organisms some that are much better fitted to endure severe environmental changes than was the parent form. It is only here, in the accidental development of increased independence of environment, of increased physiological freedom, in Bernard's sense of the word, that we can speak of evolution as being upwards, rather than just sideways.

The paleontological record reveals that evolution has not been a continuous process, but an intermittent one. In Lull's[21, 22] descriptive terms, it has been a tide of organic specialization moving forward in marked pulsations invariably synchronous with the great upheavals of the earth's crust. It was probably one of these pulsations, synchronous with the Cambrian Revolution, that gave the vertebrates their start. The more important steps in the phylogenetic history of these forms, with special reference to those events that have a close bearing upon the evolution of the kidney, are depicted graphically in Figure 1.

The problem of the origin of the first chordates remains more or less where it was left by the great biologists of the past century—in a sadly unsatisfactory state. A few years ago there was consensus of opinion on at least one point: that the chordates shared with the echinoderms, the acorn worms, Branchiostoma (Amphioxus) and the tunicates, a common marine ancestor, a frail-bodied, ghostly form, similar perhaps to the Dipleurula larva of the echinoderms.[26] The most important features of this hypothetical ancestor were that it possessed a bilateral symmetry comparable to that of Branchiostoma, and like Branchiostoma it kept one end foremost as it swam slowly and feebly through the archaic seas. But the right of this ghostly form, the like of which no one has ever seen, to spawn the great vertebrate phylum has recently been questioned on the ground that the chordates, as they first appear in the fossil record, were depressed, bottom-living, heavily armored and sluggish animals as far removed in appearance from Branchiostoma as one can imagine. This fact is in part responsible for the suggestion of Torsten Gislén[10] which has been seconded by Gregory[15, 16] that the first chordates may have been evolved from a free-swimming paleozoic crinoid, or sea-lily. To this perennial debate we will add one more confusing argument of our own in a later paragraph.

As we cannot say from what forms the first chordates were evolved, neither can we with any certainty name the time of their evolution. Some would assign this evolution to the Ordovician Period, and some to the Cambrian. The opening of the Cambrian was marked by one of the most violent periods of mountain building the earth has ever known. These mountains have long since been washed away, but the sediment to which they were reduced is to be seen in the several vertical miles of red and yellow-banded rocks through which the Colorado River has cut the Grand Caynon, and from which scenic chasm the geologic revolution takes its name. The biologist has repeatedly asserted that the truly unique features of the vertebrates consist, broadly speaking, of bilateral symmetry: of a stiffened and yet flexible internal backbone with an articulated skeleton for the support of muscles so arranged as to produce powerful lateral motions of the body, the backbone, skeleton and muscles being made up of regularly repeated segments; of paired, fin-like expansions of the skin to resist the thrust of these muscles and to maintain an even keel as the animal shoves itself forward in the water; and, of major sense organs located in the anterior end of the body. These features are just such as to endow the organism with considerable swimming power, to enable it to move swiftly through the sea, or, as an alternative, to live in a swiftly flowing river. According to one theory, first propounded by Chamberlain[5] and substantially supported by Barrell,[1] the sluggish ancestors of the chordates had already migrated from the sea into the

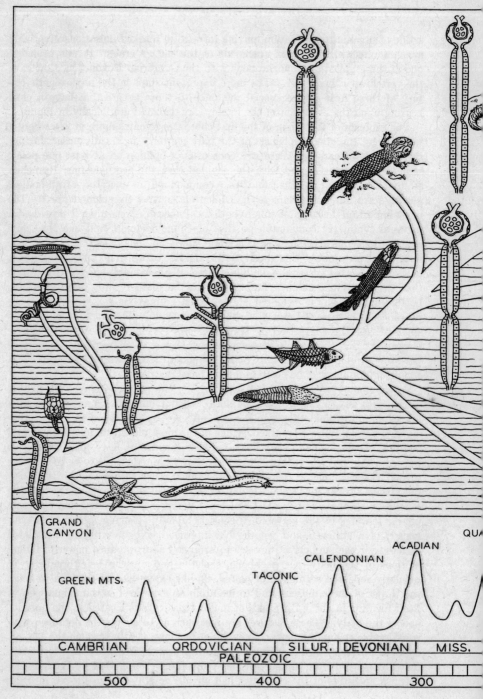

GRAND
CANYON

QUA

ACADIAN

CALENDONIAN

GREEN MTS.

TACONIC

| CAMBRIAN | ORDOVICIAN | SILUR. | DEVONIAN | MISS. |

PALEOZOIC

500   400   300

Fi

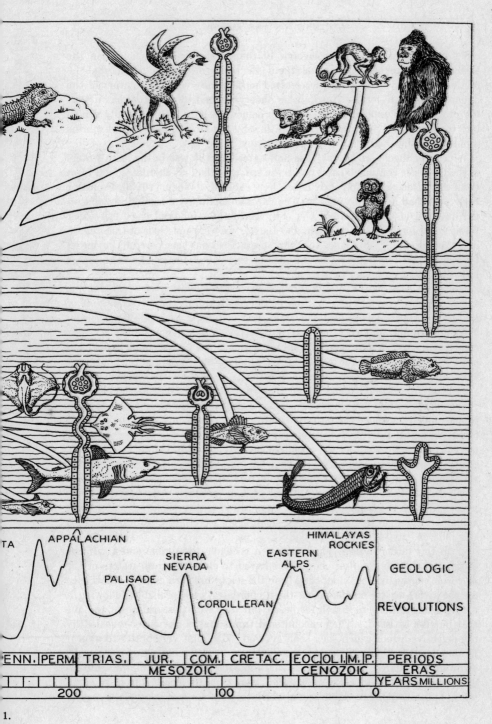

GEOLOGIC

REVOLUTIONS

| ENN. | PERM. | TRIAS. | JUR. | COM. | CRETAC. | EOC. | OLI. | M. | P. | PERIODS |
| | | | MESOZOIC | | | CENOZOIC | | | | ERAS |

200   100   0   YEARS MILLIONS

1.

quiet brackish or fresh-water lagoons of the Cambrian continents when the Grand Canyon revolution overtook them; the tilting of the land accelerated the motion of the rivers and this accelerated motion fostered the evolution of the dynamic, chordate form. But another theory, offered by Moody,[24] has it that the prochordates appeared in fresh water somewhat later, being literally driven into the rivers and lakes in Ordovician time by the attacks of the giant marine cephalopods that had then risen to supremacy in the seas.

Whichever theory we accept, it is now agreed that it was in the fresh waters of the Paleozoic continents, and not in the sea, that the first chordates, and from them the ostracoderms and early fishes, were evolved. When, in 1930, Professor E. K. Marshall and I reviewed the comparative anatomy of the kidney and on the question of the habitat of the early vertebrates followed the fresh-water thesis as set forth by Chamberlain and Barrel,[1] we were conscious of treading on uncertain ground.[23] But since that time the subject has been carefully reviewed by Romer and Grove,[27] and in the face of this new evidence the fresh water hypothesis can no longer be denied.

Now, the very matrix of life is water, and the evolution of the kidney is essentially the story of the evolution of the regulation of the water content of the body. Marine invertebrates—worms, star-fish, molluscs, etc.—are generally in osmotic equilibrium with the sea, and they therefore face no problem of water regulation. And it may safely be assumed that in the Cambrian or Ordovician prochordate ancestor of the vertebrates the kidney was little, if at all, concerned with the excretion of water, but wholly with the excretion of nitrogenous waste.

Judging from the evidence of comparative anatomy, the marine ancestor of the chordates had in each of the middle segments of the body a pair of open tubules which connected the primitive body cavity, or coelome, with the exterior; these segmental tubules were probably originally gonaducts serving to carry the eggs and sperm out of the coelomic cavity. Possibly before the chordate stage the coelomic membrane had come to play a part in excretion, and the segmental gonaducts which connected it with the exterior, and which were themselves formed by an evagination of the coelomic membrane, perhaps participated in the regulation of the composition of the blood by reabsorbing valuable substances from the coelomic fluid, or by secreting waste products into this fluid as it passed out of the body.

With this rather meagre equipment of a coelomic membrane and a number of segmental ducts the first chordates essayed to enter the fresh waters of the paleozoic continents. In migrating from the sea to brackish estuary and thence up the rivers to the inland lakes these chordates were probably following a protoplasmic impulse to search for peace, but they were destined never to have that impulse satisfied. They encountered trouble, as is obviously revealed by the defensive armor which they soon evolved. The first vertebrates to appear in abundance in the fossil record, the Silurian and Devonian ostracoderms, the arthrodires, antiarchs and the earliest shark-like forms bearing jaws, the acanthodians, and even the later advanced fishes, were typically encased from snout to tail in apparently impregnable armor which took the form of bony plates, scutes or scales. Any sample of the vertebrate population of Silurian-Devonian times from Pennsylvania to Spitzbergen suggests that some death-dealing enemy, swift, merciless and irresistible, lurked in every corner of the world.

Why all this heavy armor? Romer[26] has pointed out that the only visible enemies of the ostracoderms and early fishes were the eurypterids that shared with them the continental waterways. Admittedly some of these eurypterids were much larger than the ostracoderms and fishes, and possessed strong claws, but they were primarily sluggish mud crawlers and unless they struck with their pointed tails, as does their enfeebled descendant, *Limulus*, or injected poison, as do their offspring, the scorpions, their fearsomeness may have been more apparent than real. The thesis that the armor of the early vertebrates served primarily to protect them from predacious enemies is perhaps open to question. May I offer an alternative suggestion: these vertebrates had an enemy which they could not see, but one which pursued them every minute of the day and night, and one from which there was no escape though they fled from Pennsylvania to Spitzbergen—a physical-chemical danger inherent in their new environment. When the first migrant from the sea took up residence in fresh water, its blood and tissues, bearing the physical-chemical imprint of its marine home, were rich in salts: for we may on straight extrapolation assume that at the opening of either Cambrian or Ordovician time the sea had one-half or better of its present salinity. This saline heritage might be in part erased, but it could not wholly be cast aside without re-organizing every nerve and muscle cell. The evolution of a regulated internal environment, if it had not yet begun, was imperatively imminent. For in the new fresh-water habitat the salts and proteins of the tissue cells drew water by osmotic pressure so that by degrees the organism tended to pass from excessive hydration to edema and *in extremis* to swell to death. We may confidently assert that were the osmotic infiltration of water not arrested, survival in fresh water would be impossible. The first step towards arresting the infiltration of water would naturally be to insulate the body as far as possible by a waterproof covering. Why not believe that the ever-present armor of the fossilized vertebrates of Silurian and Devonian time was a defense against the osmotic invasion of fresh water rather than against the claws and tailspines of the eurypterids?

In the history of evolution we see repeated instances where some adaptation is carried to absurd and disadvantageous overdevelopment, and perhaps an insulation serving primarily to repell fresh water may have been the genesis of spines and tubercles and other armored absurdities as would later serve to ward off strong-jawed, sharp-toothed predators such as had not yet been evolved. It seems that it was from certain of these protuberant spines that the fins were evolved. If we take this path of interpretation, we must conclude that what started out to be merely a waterproof insulation was destined to supply the fishes with fins for swimming and with spines and other armament for battle, and the tetrapods with legs with which to crawl about on land.

But to invest the body in waterproof armor entailed important changes in internal anatomy as well. The multiple segmental openings of the archaic coelomic tubules had to be obliterated, and these tubules had to be arranged to drain into the one posterior member which still pierced the now armored skin. Thus the evolution of the first archinephric duct may have been fostered by the waterproofing of the body.   Moreover, with most of the body covered by armor, a few posterior skeletal muscles had to be selected and developed in order to concentrate leverage in a powerful tail; this emphasis on the posterior segmental muscles, together with compression of the middle segments of the body cavity beneath one or a few armor sheets, would tend to obliterate the primitive segmental divisions of the coelome and to foster the development of pericardial and splanchnic cavities as they appear in the higher vertebrates.   The evolution of an armored body, the remote, articulated parts of which had to be moved in a coordinated manner, would foster the evolution of a central nervous ganglion or brain, which stood in close functional relationship to the anterior, distance receptors.   The development of armor about the head would foster the cranial articulation of mouth parts and the evolution of jaws, which, absent in the ostracoderms, are first discoverable in the mailed acanthodians of Silurian time. But these interesting speculations, and they are nothing else, lie apart from our main theme, namely that it was in seeking protection against fresh water that the first vertebrates to be preserved in the fossil record, the ostracoderms, came to be depressed, bottom-living armored creatures far removed from the hypothetical dynamic, fast-swimming prototype of classical theory.   For even under their best efforts at free swimming the early armored vertebrates found it easier to sink to the bottom and wiggle upon the mud, where indeed most of them remained until the close of the Devonian.   If the ostracoderms are viewed as a consequence of evolution in fresh water they offer less difficulty to the dynamic theory, which is recommended on so many grounds.*

Yet even thus encased in a waterproof covering, the gills, the mouth and the intestinal tract still afforded routes by which excessive quantities of water could be absorbed.   The ostracoderms and early fishes had to compensate for this excessive influx by increasing the excretion of this substance.   Their battle against fresh water was only half won.   Evolution frequently works by adapting old things to new uses, and it seems that no better way could be devised to get the surplus of water out of the body than to have the heart pump it out; and the easiest way to do this was to prepare a filtering device by bringing the pre-existing arteries into close juxtaposition with the pre-existing coelomic tubules, to form the coelomate glomerulus which, as a lobulated tuft of capillaries, still hangs free in the pericardial cavity of some of the lower vertebrates.   Later a direct connection was effected between arteries and tubules outside the coelomic cavity, to form the typical glomerulas as found in mesonephros and metanephros

---

* The essential principle of this thesis—that the exoskeleton of the ostracoderms served as insulation against fresh water, and that it was from this exoskeleton that there were evolved the spikes and other forms of armor, and later the locomotor organs, jaws, teeth, etc., of the higher fishes—has been accepted by Gregory and Raven in their paper: Studies on the Origin and Early Evolution of Paired Fins and Limbs.   Ann. New York Acad. Scien., 42: 273, 1941.

of the higher animals.   But in many recent fishes and Amphibia, the mesonephric tubules still retain their ancient connection with the body cavity.   The essential point is that the renal glomerulus was evolved independently of, and long after the evolution of the renal tubule.   And it will be recalled that in the ontogenetic development of the human embryo the glomerulus is not brought into conjunction and connected with the tubule of the metanephros until some time after this tubule has been formed; it is possible that this interval between the development of the tubule and the glomerulus is an ontogenetic recapitulation of the phylogenetic interval which separated their evolution.

But the very nature of a high-pressure filtration system permits not only water to be pumped out of the body, but also most of the osmotically active constituents of the plasma, which means all the valuable constituents except the proteins —glucose, chloride, phosphate, etc.,—for if these did not pass through the filtering bed the great osmotic pressure which they exert would effectively prevent the heart from pumping any water through this bed.   Hence, with the advent of the glomerulus it was necessary to so modify the tubules that they could reabsorb these valuable constituents from the filtrate.   Moreover, there was such an excess of water over salt to be excreted that the urine had to be almost pure water, i.e., it had to have a substantially lower osmotic pressure than the blood.   Thus, as a concomitant of the evolution of the glomerulus, there came into existence a tubule capable of reabsorbing large quantities of glucose and similar valuable substances, and capable of elaborating, by the reabsorption of salt, a urine that was hypotonic to the blood.

To whatever extent this new fresh water kidney was adequate to its time, times changed.   The restless earth began to heave again.   At the close of the Silurian another diastrophic movement disturbed its crust; no great mountains were raised in North America, but a ridge higher than the Alps was wrinkled up in Northern Europe, of which the low Calendonian mountains of Scotland are all that now remain.   Other continental areas were extensively submerged beneath the sea, and what land escaped was plagued by extremes of climate swinging between excess of rain and drought.   The fishes of the early and middle Devonian found themselves forced to choose between the invading salt water marshes and the isolated fresh-water pools which periodically contracted into stagnant swamps or hard mud flats.   Some of the more powerful elasmobranchs, perhaps now better fitted to compete with the cephalopods and other marine invertebrates, sought sanctuary by turning towards the sea; the fate of these, the first fishes to live in salt water, will be noted in a later paragraph. The more advanced of the fishes, however, in order to survive in the stagnant waters of the continents, took to swallowing air and thus invented lungs and prepared the way for the evolution of the terrestrial vertebrates.

At the close of the Devonian the earth suffered its third major upheaval in vertebrate history; the periodic dry spells of the Devonian were replaced by protracted and widespread desiccation and many of the air-breathing fishes followed the example of the Silurian elasmobranchs and abandoned fresh water for refuge in the sea where they founded the Paleozoic-Mesozoic dynasties of marine teleosts. But certain of the fresh water fishes, the Crossopterygians, learned to use their fins for feet with which to crawl from one pool to another, and thus founded the Carboniferous and Pennsylvanian Amphibia which needed to return to the water pools only occasionally to drink and to lay their eggs.

For a moment let us consider what must have happened to the bony fishes that took up life in the sea in the Carboniferous. Actually, none of these Mesozoic forms survives today; all the recent marine teleosts having been evolved since the opening of the Cenozoic era; but the physiology of recent forms is adequate to illustrate the difficulties of changing one's habitat from fresh to salt water.

With the migration from fresh to salt water the osmotic relations between organism and environment are reversed; the body tissues are less concentrated than the sea and, unless the composition of these tissues is completely overhauled, they must tend constantly to suffer osmotic dehydration and ultimate desiccation and collapse. The marine bony fishes face not a perpetual excess of water, like their fresh water ancestors, but a perpetual deficit of it. In theory they could maintain the accustomed proportion of salt and water in the body by excreting a highly concentrated urine, but in practice they cannot do this for the fish kidney is unable to elaborate a urine which is osmotically more concentrated than the blood. Their lot would be as unhappy as that of the Ancient Mariner were it not that, unlike that thirsty man, they have the happy advantage of possessing gills, and the gill is the only organ in the lower vertebrates capable of doing hypertonic osmotic work. Had the Ancient Mariner possessed such a marvelous organ he could have lived like a fish by drinking the briny sea; he could have separated the salt from the water by excreting the salt out of his gills in a concentrated form, leaving the water free for his tissues, or for the formation of urine. But with the limitations of the fish kidney he still would have had cause to deplore his lot, since for every liter of urine formed he would be forced to concentrate a liter of sea water by 66 per cent. It is not surprising that the marine fishes, rather than spend their precious energy in making more concentrated the already concentrated sea, naturally became conservative in the matter of urine formation and excreted no more urine than was required to remove waste products from the body.[31] When the bony fishes migrated from fresh water to the sea, the high-pressure filtering device of the glomerulus was no longer an asset, but a liability. They shut the filtering bed down as far as possible, and with the passing years the glomeruli grew smaller and smaller, fewer and fewer; to examine the glomeruli in a series of marine teleost kidneys reminds one of the old-fashioned Herpecide advertisement: Going—going—gone! Nearly all the marine teleosts show some evidence of glomerular degeneration, and in certain of them (the toadfish, midshipman, goosefish, batfish, sea horse, pipefish, and in certain deep sea fishes) the kidney has become entirely aglomerular.[8, 12, 13, 14, 23] There is no constant rule by which the aglomerular condition is reached; Grafflin[11] has shown that in the "daddy" sculpin the glomeruli cease to function between the young and the adult stage, while Armstrong (personal communication) has shown that in the toadfish and pipefish a glomerulus does not develop even in the embryo. Though evolution is not reversible, the marine teleosts are indirectly converting their kidneys back to the purely tubular form possessed by the prochordate ancestor which left the sea in Cambrian or Ordovician time.

But there is more than one way of solving physiological difficulties, including that faced by the Ancient Mariner and the marine teleosts. Let us return to the elasmobranchs, who had first made the marine migration in the Devonian. These more primitive fishes solved the problem of living in salt water in an entirely different way. The four orders of the sub-class Elasmobranchii—the sharks, rays, skates and chimaeras—separated from the parent stem and from each other in or shortly after the Devonian period; that is to say, the Devonian is the most recent time at which we can assign to all four orders a common ancestry. Yet all four orders possess a common and surprisingly unique adaptation for living in seawater; they have changed the composition of their blood by deliberately bringing themselves, as it were, into a perpetually uremic state; they reabsorb from the glomerular filtrate as it passes down the tubules such urea as is present in this fluid (urea being the chief product of nitrogen combustion) much as the Ordovician-Silurian fishes learned to reabsorb glucose and chloride. They return this otherwise inert waste product to the blood until it reaches concentrations of 2000 to 2500 mgm. per cent. The presence of this urea raises the osmotic pressure of the blood above that of the surrounding sea water and causes water to move from the sea into the body, through the gills; and thus, pure water, free from salt, moves continuously inward at a sufficient rate to afford a vehicle for the urinary excretion of waste products and such excess salt as is present in the food.[32, 33] Where the bony fishes must continuously drink sea water in a steady stream, in the elasmobranchs this fluid serves only to wet the gills.

A unique tubular segment is present in the elasmobranch kidney, just distal to the glomerulus, which is thought to be the site of the active reabsorption of urea from the glomerular filtrate. None of the elasmobranch fishes, in spite of their long residence in the sea, is aglomerular; having always had abundant water available for filtration, there has been no need to abandon their glomeruli.

It is especially interesting that the method of reproduction in this subclass is highly specialized, the majority of the Elasmobranchii being viviparous, the rest producing an egg inclosed in a relatively impermeable egg case. The latter is apparently the more primitive mode of reproduction. Both the viviparous forms and those that have a cleidoic or "closed" egg utilize internal fertilization, for which purpose there exist claspers in the male and accessory reproductive glands in the female. One supposes that this specialized mode of reproduction is concerned with the conservation of urea in the young embryo until such time as its kidneys and its respiratory and integumentary membranes are organized. The Cladoselachii of the Devonian apparently lacked claspers, but these were present in the Carboniferous and Permian hybodonts and pleuracanths and in all the Jurassic sharks. Further paleontological research may, in the above view, be able to reveal to us the exact time at which the uremic habitus, as an adaptation to salt water, was acquired.

Returning now from the fishes to the main evolutionary tree: during the coal ages the low-lying lands were heavily clothed in tropical and subtropical vegetation. There was a high rainfall, the air was humid, the world was a swampy paradise inhabited by spiders, scorpions, centipedes and snails, and lorded over by Amphibia that lived half in water and half on land. But on the whole life was as stagnant as the swamps in which it lived. It was too comfortable, and in comfort the living organism comes to rest, its evolution stops or regression begins.

The moist paradise of the coal ages lasted until the Permian; then in the great Appalachian Revolution à majestic range of mountains, 3 to 4 miles high, was corrugated in the region that now lies between Newfoundland and Alabama. The Southern Hemisphere passed into a severe glacial period, and in the Northern Hemisphere the warm moist climate of the Carboniferous was replaced by aridity and seasonal chilliness. The cycads, equisetums, clubmosses and tree ferns of the coal measures were exterminated; all the great families of the marine elasmobranchs were destroyed along with most of the marine and fresh water teleosts; and the stagnant Amphibia changed slowly towards more terrestrial forms. It was the sheer pressure of world-wide Permian desiccation that fostered the evolution of the reptiles, which were driven *in extremis* to living permanently on land. These new reptiles had tough hides and relatively long legs with which to crawl from one water hole to another; the egg, for the first time in vertebrate history, was encased in a waterproof shell and contained within it the allantoic sac to receive the waste products of the embryo; a multitude of adaptations, most of which concern the preservation of the internal environment, had to be effected to liberate the organism from its primeval aquatic environment. One of the most important of these adaptations consisted in a subtle change in the method of protein combustion. Instead of degrading protein nitrogen to urea, as had the fishes and Amphibia, the reptiles overhauled their metabolic machinery and degraded their protein nitrogen to uric acid. Uric acid is a very peculiar substance: it is almost insoluble in water, and yet it readily forms highly supersaturated solutions; the reptiles secrete it in the tubular urine as a concentrated, supersaturated solution; then, as the tubular urine passes to the cloaca, the uric acid precipitates out, leaving most of the water in the urine free to be reabsorbed into the blood, while the uric acid itself is expelled as an almost dry paste. This same uric acid adaptation, like so many other reptilian characters, is found in the birds,[19, 35] for the birds are but warm blooded reptiles with feathers and wings.

When the teleosts risked desiccation in the briny sea many of them completely discarded their glomeruli as extravagant routes of water loss. In view of the fact that in the arid-living reptiles and the marine birds the need for water conservation is equally extreme one might expect some of them to be aglomerular too, but no aglomerular reptile or bird has thus far been described. The reptilian-avian kidney is, however, headed in that direction, for the once elaborate glomerular tuft is reduced to a few, in some cases only two, capillary loops, and contains a great amount of inert connective tissue. It is as though these animals, having found the glomeruli largely superfluous but needing to flush the uric acid-rich secretion of the tubules down to the cloaca, had stopped short of the complete obliteration of the glomeruli and retained a vestige of the filtering bed in order to supply the tubules with a feeble, irrigating stream.

At this point you are probably wondering if the title of this discourse is not misrepresenting, since so much of it has been devoted to the lower vertebrates and so little of it to the mammals or to man. I would defend this apparent unfairness by pointing out that all the mammals together constitute but a small fraction of the vertebrates, and man himself but one mammalian species among thousands. The geological age of truly human forms is at most 1,000,000 years, a slight interval indeed out of the 500 to 600 million years which we must apprehend if we are to see the human organism in the proper perspective. But apart from this aspect of the problem I must confess that at this point in the story of the evolution of the kidney there is a serious hiatus in our knowledge, namely, the circumstances surrounding the evolution of the first mammalian forms.

The mammals have added the only important patent to the kidney since Devonian time: the capacity to excrete urine that is markedly hypertonic, or osmotically more concentrated than the blood. As pointed out in an earlier paragraph, the elaboration of this hypertonic urine is in part effected by the unique, intermediate thin segment which is present in the tubule of all mammalian forms.

We must inquire, how did this capacity to excrete a hypertonic urine come to be evolved? And we may go on to ask, since the mammals were evolved from reptilian forms, why do they not excrete uric acid like the reptiles and the birds? And since the mammals do not generally live in fresh water, since in fact some mammals, such as the kangaroo rat, can live indefinitely upon dry oatmeal, while others, such as the whales and seals, can live indefinitely in the sea without ever taking a drink of fresh water, why have they not lost their glomeruli? Why, on the contrary, have the glomeruli reached their fullest development in the order Mammalia?

Let us review briefly what is known about early mammalian evolution. Through all the Mesozoic the mammals remained in the background and let the reptiles have the stage. During the desiccation of the Permian these thick-skinned animals, their legs ever growing longer, began to crawl on their bellies all over the world and to establish their reputation for grotesquerie. In the Triassic, which was, like the Permian, a period of aridity but one lacking marked seasonal extremes of heat and cold and generally warm enough to permit the luxuriant growth of ferns, tree ferns and equisetums, reptilian peculiarities began to reach extremes. The more advanced took to walking on their hind legs and strutted about like the lords of the universe. In the Jurassic the climate reverted to subtropical humidity, and the reptilian paradise was but slightly disturbed by the diastrophic movement that raised the Sierra Nevadas and ushered in the

Cretaceous. Here reptilian evolution culminated, on the one hand, in the great dinosaurs, the most magnificent creatures and probably the dumbest per kilogram of body weight that the earth has ever seen, and, on the other hand, in the flying reptiles whose jaws were still filled with teeth and whose wings were still tipped with claws. Then, at the end of the Cretaceous, when the Rocky Mountains and the Andes were rising slowly, the curtain is rung down on this Mesozoic scene with a suddenness that is almost dramatic. The dinosaurs disappeared, the birds lost their teeth and shaped their forelimbs into delicate wings, and a host of new actors, in the form of the Cenozoic mammals, rushed upon the stage as though they had long been waiting impatiently behind the scenes.

Where these mammals had been throughout the long and fantastic period of the Mesozoic is still a mystery. The oldest known mammalian fossils date from the late Triassic or early Jurassic periods, and these were already advanced and specialized creatures; no remnants of a stock which could have been ancestral even to the Cretaceous forms have been discovered.[30] However, it must be believed that truly mammalian types were in existence in the early Triassic, and probably even in the Permian, while the reptiles themselves were still in a relatively primitive stage. Certain Triassic reptiles, the cynodonts, resembled the mammals in such features as the posterior jaw elements, the teeth and the structure of the shoulder girdle, and they stood with their limbs well under the body, and it may be supposed that the cynodont reptiles and the mammals were evolved out of a common Permian stock. It need not be supposed, however, that this common ancestral stock was warm-blooded, or need it be supposed that it had acquired the reptilian habit of excreting uric acid; rather it may have been a semi-aquatic type that degraded its protein nitrogen to urea, as we may suppose was the case in the Pennsylvanian Amphibia.

Proceeding from this premise, it is to be noted that there were two environmental stresses operating in Permian time: intense aridity and intense frigidity. The Permian was one of the greatest ice ages of all time. Frigidity—the cold nights of the desert and the long, cold, seasonal winters—placed a high premium upon the ability to be continuously active, even as aridity placed a premium upon the ability to travel overland from one water hole to another. A nascent, evolving stock could adapt itself to one of these stresses ahead of the other. Let us suppose that the protomammalian forms got off to warm-bloodedness first, in adaptation to frigidity, rather than to uric acid excretion, in adaptation to aridity. The progressive evolution of warm-bloodedness entailed a marked increase in the circulation of the blood, which in turn entailed a corresponding increase in arterial blood pressure; this increased blood pressure resulted in an increased rate of filtration through the glomeruli, and this entailed an increased need for conserving water by reabsorbing it from the tubules. Thus rapid elevation of body temperature would foster increased reabsorption in the tubules by accentuating the very need for it. It is plausible, therefore, that the accentuated capacity of the mammalian tubule for reabsorbing water was simply a sequel of the evolution of the warm-blooded state, which evolutionary step may have been taken before the habitus of uric acid excretion had become fixed in the general reptilian stock. Once the definitive mammalian kidney had been evolved as an adaptation to frigidity, it served as an adaptation to aridity as well, for the enhancement of water conservation which it effected enabled the mammals to compete, dry spell for dry spell, with the more sluggish reptilian forms. Into whatever dry spot the reptiles could radiate the mammals could follow them, and when the desert night descended and forced the cold-blooded reptiles into sleep the warm-blooded mammals remained active and alert. But more important, perhaps, was the change in temperature that marked the Laramide revolution; it may have been the inability of the reptiles to endure this period of refrigeration and desiccation that led to their almost total extinction,[25] while the furry warm-blooded mammals, equipped to meet both vicissitudes, could carry on.

This interpretation receives support in the fact that in the bird kidney the tubules are of a mixed type, some resembling the reptilian tubule in lacking a thin segment, some resembling the mammalian tubule in possessing such a segment. Functionally the bird kidney is intermediate between the reptiles and the mammals, the bird retaining the uric acid habitus of the former, although it can under certain conditions elaborate a distinctly hypertonic urine.[19] The similarity to the mammalian kidney in the last respect is probably a case of convergent evolution fostered by the common character of warm-bloodedness, for the birds were evolved from reptiles that were far removed from the mammalian stem.

When, at the close of the Cretaceous, the dinosaurs became extinct, the mammals began to populate the earth. In the Paleocene the lemuroids took to living in the trees and became the Eocene tarsioids who looked forward with both eyes at the same time and depended upon the sense of sight rather than upon smell or hearing. In the Oligocene a tarsioid or lemuroid stock gave rise to the monkeys which in the Miocene in turn spawned the Dryopithecine apes that roamed over Europe, Africa, and Asia. Then the rising Himalayas buckled central Asia into an uninhabitable mountain chain, and such of the Dryopithecine apes as survived were driven to abandon the trees and to seek their living in the southern plains. From Asia a Dryopithecine descendant migrated into Africa, to spawn there in the Pliocene such forms as *Australopithecus africanus*, discovered by Dart,[7] and *Plesianthropus transvaalensis* and *Paranthropus robustus*, recently discovered by Broom,[3,4] and declared by their discoverers and by Gregory and Hellman[17] to be truly neither ape nor man. (For a general discussion of the origin of man see Wilder.[36])

The kidney is not identical in structure and function in all mammalian forms, but the human kidney differs only in details from that organ in the dog, cat, and rabbit. It is not surprising that in function the human kidney has its closest homologue in the kidneys of the great apes, who can claim with man a common ancestor back somewhere in the Miocene.

Examining the pattern of the human kidney, we must not be surprised to find that it is far from a perfect organ. In fact, it is in many respects grossly inefficient. It begins its task by pouring some 125 cc. of water into the tubules each minute, demanding for this extravagant filtration one quarter of all the blood put out by the heart. Out of this stream of water, 99 per cent must be reabsorbed again. This circuitous method of operation is peculiar, to say the least. At one end, the heart is working hard to pump a large quantity of water out of the body; at the other end the tubules are working equally hard to defeat the heart by keeping 99 per cent of this water from escaping. Thus heart and kidney are literally pitched in constant battle against each other—our lives depend on neither one of them ever winning out. Nature frequently opposes two forces against each other in order to maintain a steady state, but the opposition in this instance takes on an aspect of sheer extravagance. Paradoxically, the kidney has to do its greatest work when it excretes the smallest quantity of urine; as the urine flow increases it does less and less work, and if the urine flow were to increase to the colossal figure of 125 per minute—170 liters per day— the kidney, in respect to the excretion of water, would be doing no work at all.

In consequence of the circuitous pattern of the filtration and reabsorption of water, nearly half-a-pound of glucose and over three pounds of sodium chloride per day, not to mention quantities, of phosphate, amino acids and other substances, must be saved from being lost in the urine by being reabsorbed from the tubular stream. There is enough waste motion here to bankrupt any economic system—other than a natural one, for Nature is the only artificer who does not need to count the cost by which she achieves her ends.

The chief waste product which the kidney is called upon to excrete is urea. The glomeruli remove each minute such urea as is contained in 125 cc. of blood, but because of the way the tubules are put together fifty per cent of this urea diffuses back into the blood again, so that in terms of the total renal blood flow (1200 cc. per minute) the over-all efficiency of the excretion is only about 5 per cent. There are certain foreign substances, however (diodrast, hippuran, phenol red, etc.), which have been synthetized only within the past few years, which the kidney excretes with almost 100 per cent efficiency. Is it not strange that, in spite of the fact that it has never before encountered them, the kidney should be able to excrete such artificial, synthetic compounds twenty times as efficiently as it excretes the principal nitrogenous waste product naturally formed in the body, and which it has been excreting for millions and millions of years?

The kidney is receiving more attention today than ever before. These scientific problems range from local organic pathology to such subtle matters as the relation of the internal environment and its multiplicity of chemical factors to personality and mental disease. Certainly, mental integrity is a *sine qua non* of the free and independent life. As intermittent rays of light blend into moving images on the cinematographic screen, so the multiform activities within the brain are integrated into images of consciousness and brought into an unstable focus to form that fleeting entity which we call personality, or Self. But let the composition of our internal environment suffer change, let our kidneys fail for even a short time to fulfill their task, and our mental integrity, our personality, is destroyed.

There are those who say that the human kidney was created to keep the blood pure, or more precisely, to keep our internal environment in an ideal balanced state. I would deny this. I grant that the human kidney is a marvelous organ, but I cannot grant that it was purposefully designed to excrete urine, or even to regulate the composition of the blood, or to subserve the physiological welfare of *Homo sapiens* in any sense. Rather I contend that the human kidney manufactures the kind of urine that it does, and it maintains the blood in the composition which that fluid has, because this kidney has a certain functional architecture: and it owes that architecture not to design or foresight or any plan, but to the fact that the earth is an unstable sphere with a fragile crust, to the geologic revolutions that for 600 million years have raised and lowered continents and seas, to the predacious enemies, and heat and cold, and storms and droughts, the unending succession of vicissitudes that have driven the mutant vertebrates from sea into fresh water, into desiccated swamps, out upon the dry land, from one habitation to another, perpetually in search of the free and independent life, perpetually failing for one reason or another to find it.

It is more than an antiquarian impulse that leads me to close this lecture by two quotations. About the 5th century, a Persian philosopher who is well known to all of you remarked:

"Myself when young did eagerly frequent
Doctor and Saint, and heard great argument
    about it and about: but evermore
Came out by the same door where in I went."

Many centuries later, specifically in 1804, a French chemist named Fourcroy,[9] who presented the first comprehensive exposition of the nature and physiological importance of urine in a volume entitled, "A General System of Chemical Knowledge", said:

"The urine of man is one of the animal matters that have been the most examined by chemists and of which the examination has at the same time furnished the most singular discoveries to chemistry, and the most useful applications to physiology, as well as the art of healing. This liquid, which commonly inspires men only with contempt and disgust, which is generally ranked amongst vile and repulsive matters, has become, in the hands of the chemists, a source of important discoveries and is an object in the history of which we find the most singular disparity between the ideas which are generally formed of it in the world, and the valuable notion which the study of it affords to the physiologist, the physician and the philosopher."

BIBLIOGRAPHY

The following list is not so much intended to encompass the literature in this field as to indicate a few articles or books of special interest to the student of general biology.

1. BARRELL, J. 1916. Influence of Silurian-Devonian climates on the rise of air-breathing vertebrates. Bull. Geol. Soc. Amer., *27*, 387.
2. BERNARD, C. 1878. Leçons sur les phénomènes de la vie communs aux animaux et aux végétaux. Paris, J. B. Ballière et fils.
3. BROOM, R. 1936. A new fossil anthropoid skull from South Africa. Nature, *138*, 486.

4. BROOM, R. 1938. The Pleistocene anthropoid apes of South Africa. Nature, *142*, 377.
5. CHAMBERLAIN, T. C. 1900. On the habitat of the early vertebrates. J. Geol., *8*, 400.
6. DALY, R. A. 1926. Our Mobile Earth. Chas. Scribners Sons, New York.
7. DART, R. A. 1925. *Australopithecus africanus:* the man-ape of South Africa. Nature, *115*, 195.
8. EDWARDS, J. G. 1928. Studies on aglomerular and glomerular kidneys. I. Anatomical. Am. J. Anat., *42*, 75.
9. FOURCROY, A. F. 1804. A General System of Chemical Knowledge. Trans. by Wm. Nicholson. London, printed for Cadell and Davies, Etc. II volumes.
10. GISLÉN, T. 1930. Affinities between the Echinodermata, Enteropneusta, and Chordonia. Zool. Bidrag. f. Uppsala, *12*, 199.
11. GRAFFLIN, A. L. 1933. Glomerular degeneration in the kidney of the daddy sculpin (Myoxocephalus scorpius), Anat. Record, *57*, 59.
12. GRAFFLIN, A. L. 1937. The problem of adaption to fresh and salt water in the teleosts, viewed from the standpoint of the structure of the renal tubules. J. Cell. & Comp. Physiol., *9*, 469.
13. GRAFFLIN, A. L. 1937. Observations upon the aglomerular nature of certain teleostean kidneys. J. Morph., *61*, 165.
14. GRAFFLIN, A. L. 1937. The structure of the nephron in fishes. Representative types of nephron encountered; the problem of homologies among the differentiated portions of the proximal convoluted segment. Anat. Record, *68*, 287.
15. GREGORY, W. K. 1935. Reduplication in Evolution. Quart. Rev. Biol., *10*, 272.
16. GREGORY, W. K. 1936. The transformation of organic designs: a review of the origin and deployment of the earlier vertebrates. Biol. Rev., *11*, 311.
17. GREGORY, W. K. AND M. HELLMAN. 1938. Evidence of the Australopithecine man-apes on the origin of man. Science, *88*, 615.
   1939. The South African fossil man-apes and the origin of human dentition. J. Amer. Dent. Assoc., *26*, 558.
18. HOLMES, A. 1927. The Age of the Earth. Ernest Benn, Ltd., London.
19. KORR, I. M. 1939. Osmotic function of the chicken kidney. J. Cell. & Comp. Physiol., *13*, 175.
20. LONGWELL, C. R., A. KNOPF AND R. F. FLINT. 1932. A Textbook of Geology. Part I. Physical Geology. John Wiley and Sons, Inc., London.
21. LULL, R. S. 1929. The Pulse of Life. Chapter IV of The Evolution of Earth and Man. Yale University Press.
22. LULL, R. S. 1929. Organic Evolution. The Macmillan Co., New York.
23. MARSHALL, E. K. JR. AND H. W. SMITH. 1930. The glomerular development of the vertebrate kidney in relation to habitat. Biol. Bull., *59*, 135.
24. MOODIE, R. L. 1933. A Popular Guide to the Nature and the Environment of the Fossil Vertebrates of New York. New York State Museum Handbook No. 12. The University of the State of New York, Albany.
25. NOPSCA, F. 1934. The influence of geological and climatological factors on the distribution of non-marine fossil reptiles and Stegocephalia. Quart. J. Geol. Soc. London, *90*, 76.
26. ROMER, A. S. 1933. Vertebrate Paleontology. Also, Man and the Vertebrates. University of Chicago Press.
27. ROMER, A. S. AND B. H. GROVE. 1935. Environment of the early vertebrates. Amer. Midland Nat., *16*, 805.
28. SCHUCHERT, C. 1914. Climates of Geologic Time. Part II of The Climatic Factor as Illustrated in Arid America. Ellsworth Huntington. Carnegie Inst. of Wash., Pub. No. 192, pp. 265–298.
29. SCHUCHERT, C. 1929. The Earth's Changing Surface and Climate. In The Evolution of Earth and Man. Yale University Press.
30. SIMPSON, G. G. 1937. The beginning of the age of mammals. Biol. Rev., *12*, 1.

31. SMITH, H. W. 1932. Water regulation and its evolution in the fishes. Quart. Rev. of Biol., 7, 1.

32. SMITH, H. W. 1933. The functional and structural evolution of the vertebrate kidney. Sigma Xi Quart., 21, 141.

33. SMITH, H. W. 1936. The retention and physiological role of urea in the Elasmobranchii. Biol. Rev., 11, 49.

34. SMITH, H. W. 1937. The Physiology of the Kidney. Oxford University Press.

35. SHANNON, J. A. 1938. The excretion of uric acid in the chicken. J. Cell. & Comp. Physiol., 11, 135.

36. WILDER, H. H. 1926. The Pedigree of the Human Race. Henry Holt & Co., New York.

NEWER METHODS OF STUDY OF
RENAL FUNCTION IN MAN

NEWER METHODS OF STUDY OF RENAL FUNCTION IN MAN

The physiology of the kidney is so richly charged with both intrinsic interest and far-reaching implications that a speaker in this field possessing, as I do, not only limited time for exposition but limited first-hand experience, must take careful precautions against exceeding either of these limitations. In weighing my responsibility as a recipient of this lectureship I have thought that the generosity and intent of its founder could be met by confining my discussion to a few topics, rather than by attempting an extended résumé of our knowledge of renal function as a whole.

This first lecture will deal primarily with the physiological basis of recently developed methods for examining the normal and diseased kidney. It is a truism that medicine, as all other sciences, moves forward just as rapidly as do its methods, and no apology is needed for devoting so much time to this phase of the subject. The methods to which I will refer are functional methods for measuring the rate of glomerular filtration, the renal blood flow, and the quantity of intact, active glomerular and tubular tissue. The application of these methods in the examination of the action of drugs and physiological agents on renal function will serve as a logical bridge to the subject of the possible rôle of the kidneys in disease.

I think it may safely be assumed that you are thoroughly familiar with the basic principles of renal function, but we may briefly review these principles in terms of a schematic human nephron. (Figure 1). This nephron consists of a glomerulus and a subjoined tubule, the latter being divided into three major segments: a 'proximal' segment, which immediately adjoins the glomerulus and has the largest diameter, and which is made up of irregular epithelial cells with brush-like striations at their internal border; an 'intermediate' segment of smaller diameter, made up of quite flat or squamous cells; and a 'distal' segment with fairly regular columnar epithelium having striations in the basal aspect of the cell, but lacking the brush formation in the internal border. The urine formed in this nephron is conducted to the renal pelvis by way of an arborized system of collecting tubules which appear to have no function other than that of conduits. According to Moritz and Hayman[30] there are an average of 1,283,000 such nephrons in each of the human kidneys.

The blood supply to this nephron consists of an afferent arteriole which breaks up immediately within the glomerulus to form an elaborate tuft of parallel capillaries; these capillaries converge into the efferent arteriole, which in turn subdivides again to form a secondary plexus of capillaries closely applied to the external or basement membrane of the tubule cells. Until recent years it was believed that all the blood reaching the tubules must first pass through the glomeruli, but recent studies indicate that in the diseased kidney circulation in some peritubular capillaries may be established independently of the glomeruli by direct anastomoses between the arteriolar tree and either the capillary or venous channels.[54] However, the evidence is against the existence of an appreciable number of such direct connections in the normal human kidney, and they are seen to be of less importance than was once thought when it is recognized that abundant anastomoses between the peritubular capillaries, coupled with

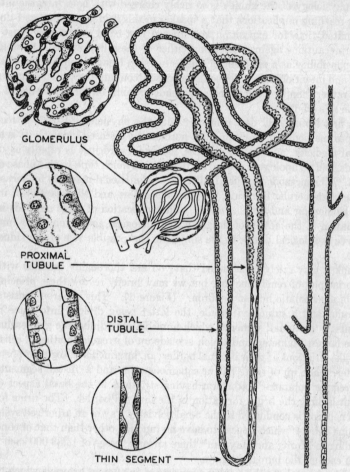

FIGURE 1. Diagrammatic representation of a human nephron.   (From 53)

circulation of interstitial fluid, will tend to maintain peritubular circulation in the face of local glomerular occlusion.[56]

Every student of renal physiology recalls Cushny's theory of urine formation. It was the cardinal premise of this theory that the formation of urine begins with the separation in the glomeruli of an ultrafiltrate identical in composition with the plasma except for the absence of the plasma proteins, to which the glomerular capillaries were presumed to be impermeable.* The actuality of this process of glomerular filtration is now established beyond the slightest doubt. The painstaking investigations of Professor Richards and his co-workers on the composition of the glomerular fluid in the frog and other cold-blooded animals, investigations begun in 1924 and only recently published in full,[34, 35, 36] have afforded incontrovertible proof of this thesis in these animals. Minute amounts of fluid have been collected from the glomerular capsule of Amphibia and reptiles by means of a Chamber's micro-dissection pipette, and by micro-analytical methods of high accuracy these minute quantities of fluid have been analyzed for various constituents. Comparison of the capsular fluid and of the plasma simultaneously circulating in the animal has demonstrated that fats and plasma proteins, or substances chemically combined with these large molecular aggregates, are the only important constituents of the plasma that do not pass through this filtering bed. Since certain substances, such as glucose and chloride, are invariably present in the capsular fluid although they may be nearly or wholly absent from the urine, these investigations also afford a direct demonstration of the actuality of tubular reabsorption—which process is, of course, a corollary of glomerular filtration. By a still more admirable technique the Philadelphia investigators have been able to follow the processes of tubular reabsorption, and to demonstrate the specific role of the proximal and distal tubules in the reabsorption of various substances.

Because of the similar anatomy of the glomerulus in frog and man, the above evidence for glomerular filtration could by inference be transferred directly to the human kidney. Actually, inferential transfer is no longer necessary, for data are now available on the excretion of a variety of substances in man which afford convincing evidence that a process of glomerular filtration, identical with that in the frog, occurs in man.

Those who recall the details of Cushny's theory will recollect that that writer was opposed to the belief that substances could be excreted directly by the tubule cells into the tubular urine without the interposition of the glomeruli. Cushny's opinion on this matter was, I believe, influenced by the conviction that such a process of tubular excretion must involve vital activity on the part of the tubule cells, a vital activity that transcended investigation and quantitation. In the previous century the doctrine of vitalism had been expelled from the physiology of nerve and muscle and, commendably, Cushny had no wish to see it regain a foothold in the physiology of the kidney. Subsequent investigations, however, have not only demonstrated that tubular excretion actually occurs, but they have shown that this process, far from being vitalistically indeterminate, is amenable to orderly, quantitative description. Recalling the many years during which tubular excretion was questioned by adherents of the Cushny theory, we may note that so far as affording us information on critical aspects of renal activity, it is more valuable than is glomerular function.

* Bott and Richards[2] have shown that the limit of permeability of the glomerular membranes is reached with protein molecules having a diameter of about 20A.

The first convincing evidence of tubular excretion appears to have been adduced by Marshall and Vickers from a study of the excretion of phenol red in the dog, but the most emphatic evidence consists of observations of Marshall and Grafflin and of Edwards and Condorelli on the aglomerular fish kidney.[25, 46] The aglomerular tubule is capable of excreting all the more important constituents normally present in fish urine: magnesium, sulfate, chloride, potassium, ammonia, creatinine, creatine, uric acid, the foreign substances, iodides, nitrites, thiosulphates and suphocyanates, and the dyes, indigocarmin, neutral red and phenol red.   There has subsequently been added to this list the organic iodine compounds, diodrast, hippuran.[10] By another technique, utilizing in vitro cultures of kidney tissue, Chambers and Kempton[5] and Cameron and Chambers[4] have afforded a direct visual demonstration of tubular excretion in the mesonephric tubule of the chick and the metanephric tubule of man.   Good evidence of the tubular excretion of urea in the frog has been advanced by Marshall[25] and independently by Höber.[19]

The data now available on man leave no doubt that tubular excretion plays a very important part in the excretion of phenolred,[15] diodrast, hippuran,[23, 58] and various other substituted hippuric acid derivatives, iopax, neoiopax, skiodan[60] and creatinine,[24, 40, 50] but even prior to these demonstrations the possibility of tubular excretion in man had to be accepted on inference.   Cytologically, the aglomerular tubule appears to be roughly homologous with the proximal segment of the human nephron and, without implying a perfect parallel in function, the demonstration that the aglomerular tubule can excrete a large variety of substances made it necessary to assume, in the absence of evidence to the contrary, that the human tubule might also be able to excrete them.   Since, by the filtration-reabsorption mechanism of the nephron, the glomerular filtrate undergoes a variable degree of concentration by the reabsorption of water, it is impossible to determine directly from the composition of blood and urine whether the excretion of any one of several substances involves filtration alone, or filtration plus either tubular reabsorption or tubular excretion.   Once tubular excretion was admitted as a possibility, it was clear that the unravelling of the problems of renal function could not advance beyond the stage of speculation, whether nephrons were investigated individually or en masse, until there was available at least one substance which was known for certain to be neither excreted nor reabsorbed by the tubule cells.   Once such a substance had been discovered, it could be used as a standard of reference with which to measure the tubular reabsorption of water, and hence to examine the mechanism of excretion of any other substance. Since this question cannot be answered in any instance by direct comparison of the absolute quantity of substance filtered with the quantity ultimately excreted, there remains as the only method of examination a comparison of the rates of excretion of various substances relative to their respective plasma concentrations.

It was with the recognition of these facts that observations on the relative rates of excretion of various substances in the dog were begun in my laboratory by Jolliffe and Shannon in 1929.   We started from Marshall's[25] observation that the aglomerular kidney cannot under any circumstances excrete glucose; presumably the tubule cells have in their evolution never acquired the capacity to excrete this valuable foodstuff. But even assuming that the human tubule is also unable to excrete glucose, nevertheless this tubule is obviously able to reabsorb it, since glucose must be present in the glomerular filtrate even though it is absent from the urine. Consequently we turned to the various non-metabolized carbohydrates, substances which are relatively inert and which are copiously excreted by the kidneys, as representing the type of compound most likely to fulfill the physiological specifications for measuring directly the degree of water reabsorption. Since it is inadvisable to draw conclusions from a single species, these investigations, as indeed nearly all our investigations since, were extended to several species, principally the dogfish, the dog, and man. The dogfish was chosen because it is the lowest of the vertebrates which lends itself to experimental investigation; it has, moreover, certain unique features such as the capacity to actively conserve urea which make it a critical testing-ground for any theory. The dog kidney very closely resembles the human kidney in its functional capacities, and very accurate quantitative observations can be made upon trained, unanesthetized dogs. And in the last analysis every conclusion reached from a study of the lower animals must, of course, be put to its final test in man. In addition to these three species, numerous supplementary observations have been made on the sculpin, chicken, rabbit, sheep, seal, monkey and the anthropoid apes.[53] A wide foundation of comparative physiology is essential if we are to interpret with confidence details of function in the human kidney.

Successive studies of the simultaneous excretion rates of carbohydrates and other substances led to inulin, a starch-like polysaccharide composed of 32 hexose molecules (mostly fructose) and having a molecular weight of 5200.[54] Because of the elongate nature of the molecule, its diffusion coefficient is considerably less than would be expected from its molecular size, being only twice as great as hemoglobin. It is completely filterable from plasma through collodion membranes, but it is about as large a molecule as one would expect to filter through the glomeruli. It is physiologically inert and rapidly and quantitatively excreted in the urine.

The long series of experiments upon which the use of inulin is based have been reviewed elsewhere[53] and only the more important ones need be mentioned here. It has been shown that inulin and exogenous creatinine (endogenous creatinine in most animals is apparently a mixture of several substances which give the Jaffé reaction) when examined in simultaneous blood and urine samples are concentrated to precisely the same degree in the dog,[41, 42] rabbit,[22] seal,[52] sheep[43] and frog.[12] Since it is improbable that two substances as different as inulin and creatinine would be either excreted or reabsorbed by the tubules to precisely the same extent in these different species of animals, it may be accepted that in these species both substances are excreted by filtration without tubular participation.

But the concentration ratio of creatinine is very much higher than that of inulin in the dogfish,[39] the red grouper,[31] the chicken,[44] and the anthropoid apes.[57] This discrepancy is also evident in man; when creatinine is freshly injected into the blood it is concentrated by the human kidney about 40 per cent more than is inulin;[24, 27, 40, 50] here either 40 per cent of the inulin is reabsorbed, or considerable creatinine is excreted by the tubules in addition to that which is filtered.   However, the simultaneous concentration ratios of inulin, sorbitol, mannitol and sor-

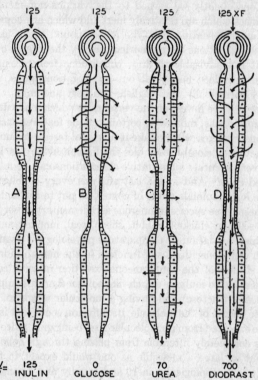

FIGURE 2. Scheme to illustrate the excretion of (A) inulin, which is excreted solely by filtration with no tubular reabsorption; (B) glucose, which is filtered, but at normal plasma level and rate of filtration is completely reabsorbed by the tubule; (C) urea, which is filtered, but in part escapes from the tubular urine by diffusion; (D) diodrast, which is excreted both by filtration and tubular excretion. UV/P is the clearance in each instance, i.e., the virtual volume of blood cleared per minute.   (U and P are the concentrations per unit volume of urine and plasma, and V is urine flow per minute.)   The inulin clearance is taken as equal to the rate of filtration of plasma.   F is the fraction of diodrast filterable from the plasma, 1.00-F being the fraction bound to plasma proteins.

bitan are identical in both dog and man,[59] from which it may be inferred that the discrepancy between inulin and creatinine is attributable to the tubular excretion of creatinine, rather than to the tubular reabsorption of inulin.*   The ques-

* Steinitz[62] reports that the concentration ratios of sucrose and inulin are identical in man, though the earlier studies of Jolliffe, Shannon and Smith[20, 21] indicated that about 20 per cent of the filtered sucrose was reabsorbed, since the clearances check with xylose. In phlorizinized man, however, Chasis, Jolliffe and Smith[6] found that the glucose, xylose and sucrose clearances are identical.   The situation in the dog is depicted in Figure 4.

tion is an important one, since on the basis of Rehberg's[33] early investigations, the creatinine clearance has been widely accepted, especially in Europe, as a measure of glomerular filtration in man. However, the difference between the creatinine and inulin clearances may be as much as 70 per cent immediately after creatinine administration, this difference decreasing with the lapse of time apparently because some of the creatinine is transformed to an unidentified substance which is less readily excreted by the tubules.[40, 46,50]

Independently of our investigations with inulin in a variety of species, Richards and his co-workers, led by the same considerations as ourselves, were examining the excretion of this substance in the frog, Necturus and the dog. Hendrix, Westfall and Richards[18] showed that it is completely filterable through the glomeruli of the frog and Necturus. Richards, Westfall and Bott[38] and Van Slyke, Hiller and Miller[63] have confirmed the observation that in the dog these two substances have identical concentration ratios within the limits of analytical error. More recently, Richards, Bott and Westfall[37] have added to the evidence against tubular excretion of inulin in the frog, rabbit and dog, by perfusing the kidneys of these animals with blood at pressures too low to permit glomerular filtration to occur. Under these conditions hippuran and phenol red, which are indubitably excreted by tubules, accumulate in the tubular urine whereas inulin and creatinine do not.

Deferring for the moment a further discussion of the excretion of inulin in man, we will tentatively assume that this polysaccharide is filterable through the glomeruli in the same concentration per unit of water as it is present in the plasma; thereafter it passes down the tubules suffering neither increase or decrease in amount in consequence of tubular excretion or tubular reabsorption. It follows that the degree of water reabsorption is revealed by the inulin urine/plasma (U/P) ratio, and also that the rate of glomerular filtration is given by the quantity of inulin excreted per minute (UV) divided by the concentration in each cc. of plasma (P). (See Figure 2a). The filtration rate in man, measured in this manner, averages 131 per minute.[56] This figure is not surprisingly large when we consider that the total surface area of the glomerular capillary bed, as calculated from Book's[1] data on a typical glomerulus, is nearly 1.0 square meter. Out of this 131 cc. of water filtered through the glomerulus, 130 are on the average reabsorbed by the tubules, leaving only 1 cc. to be excreted in the urine. In consequence of the variable reabsorption of water, inulin (and of course other substances) appears in the urine in variable concentrations, but variations in urine flow or the degree of urine concentration do not normally entail any change in the rate of filtration itself.[7]

Returning to the overall operation of the kidney, we may say that it is the function of this organ to clear the blood flowing through it of various substances, and that the overall efficiency of this clearance process in any instance depends upon the specific mechanism of excretion, which in turn will depend upon the properties of the substance under examination.

Rewording the above, we may say that inulin is cleared from the plasma exclusively by a process of filtration, unmodified by tubular reabsorption or tubular excretion.   Hence the volume of plasma cleared of inulin in each minute's time must be equal to the rate of filtration itself.

To extend this idea to other substances, we may say that glucose (Figure 2b) is initially cleared from the plasma by filtration at a rate identical with that of inulin, but because all the glucose is normally actively reabsorbed by the tubules the volume of plasma which is cleared of glucose per minute's time in the overall operation is zero.   Urea (Figure 2c) is likewise initially cleared from the plasma at a rate identical with that of inulin, but about 50 per cent of this filtered urea escapes from the tubular urine by passive diffusion and consequently only half as much plasma is actually cleared of urea as is cleared of inulin.   Diodrast (Figure 2d) is cleared from the blood both by filtration and tubular excretion, and hence a much larger volume of plasma is cleared of this substance per minute than could be cleared by filtration alone.

Thus we may speak of the inulin 'clearance' (= filtration rate) the glucose 'clearance', the urea 'clearance' and the diodrast 'clearance', as the virtual volume of plasma which is cleared of these particular substances in one minute's time.   This virtual volume is quite simply calculated by dividing the quantity of substance excreted in one minute's time (UV) by the quantity contained in each cc. of plasma.*

I have made this round-about approach to the concept of clearance, because it has been my experience that as soon as the word is mentioned, there may occur one of two adverse reactions: the auditor may infer that a clearance is just another empirical renal function test, of which there have been plenty in the history of renal physiology; or, discovering that a 'clearance' involves an arithmetical calculation based upon concentrations in blood and the rate of excretion, he may conclude that it is incomprehensible to the non-mathematically minded.   Neither inference is correct; the mathematics involved is but simple arithmetic, and the calculation is the only physiological and logical method of evaluating the overall activity of the kidney in clearing the blood of any particular substance.   One point which sometimes adds confusion to the notion of renal clearances is this: the word 'clearance' was introduced into renal physiology in 1928 by Möller, Mackintosh and Van Slyke[28] as an empirical means of describing the excretion of urea, which is dependent upon the rate of urine flow.   Variations in urine flow arise from variations in the amount of water reabsorbed from the glomerular filtrate by the tubules and, in consequence of the variable degree of concentration of the urea in the tubular urine, a variable quantity of the filtered urea diffuses back across the tubules.[42]   Hence the urea clearance decreases with decreasing urine flow.   But this is not true of inulin or of other substances with which we will be concerned here; we may therefore divorce the concept of renal clearance from

* Since most of the substances with which we are concerned do not penetrate the red cells but are carried to the kidneys solely by the plasma, it is desirable, in order to avoid errors due to variable hematocrit, to make all clearance calculations on the basis of the concentration of substance in plasma rather than whole blood, and to call such clearance, 'plasma clearance.'

all association with urine volume *per se* and identify it with the initial excretory operations of the glomeruli and tubules.

Let us now examine the clearances of various substances in normal man, these clearances being measured when the substances are present in the plasma at suitably low concentrations, as shown at the left of Figure 3. These clearances vary upwards from 0.0 to slightly above 700 cc. of plasma per minute. The glucose clearance, of course, is zero because at normal plasma levels the filtered glucose is all reabsorbed by the tubules. The same may be said of vitamin C, and the various other substances not shown in the figure, such as amino acids, uric acid, sodium, potassium, chloride and SO_4; all of these substances have been

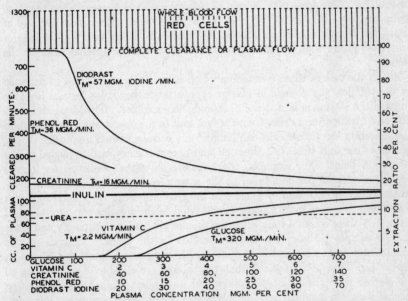

FIGURE 3. Diagrammatic summary of excretion of various types of compounds by the human kidney. The quantitative relations are fully described in the text.

demonstrated to be completely filterable from plasma, and their low clearances must be attributed to tubular reabsorption. The urea clearance (plasma) averages about 70 cc., inulin,[56] 131 cc., creatinine,[40] 175 cc., phenol red, 400 cc.,[15] and diodrast, 697 cc. per minute.[56] From what has been said above, we may infer that the various values of these clearances reveal differences in the mechanism by which these substances are excreted. Accepting the conclusion that the inulin clearance is equal to the rate of glomerular filtration, it follows that substances such as Na, K, Cl, amino acids, glucose and vitamin C, the clearances of which are less than the inulin clearance, must be reabsorbed by the tubules (providing of course that they are filterable through the glomeruli), while substances such as creatinine, phenol red, iopax, hippuran and diodrast, the clearances of which are greater than the inulin clearance, must be excreted by the tubules in addition to being filtered through the glomeruli.

I have chosen to present a comprehensive picture of renal function in one diagram because it enables us to grasp quickly certain fundamental principles. We can discover important facts about these processes of tubular absorption and excretion by observing what happens to these several clearances when the plasma concentration is changed. Changing the plasma concentration of inulin has no effect on the inulin clearance, since whatever inulin is present in the glomerular filtrate is passed on into the urine regardless of whether it is a large or small amount.[26, 51] The same may be said of urea; the urea clearance is less than the inulin clearance because of diffusion out of the tubules rather than because of active reabsorption, and this process of diffusion is determined by the rate of urine flow rather than by the concentration of urea in the tubular urine or the blood.

But in the case of those substances which are actively reabsorbed or excreted by the tubules, any change in plasma concentration beyond a critical level influences the clearance in a definite, reproducible manner. This dependence on the concentration term arises from the fact that in the operations of reabsorption and excretion the tubule cells can handle only certain limited quantities of any substance per unit time; i.e., these cellular operations are readily loaded to the saturation point. For example, the tubule cells cannot reabsorb an infinite amount of glucose per unit time; as the plasma concentration of glucose is increased the concentration of glucose in the glomerular filtrate is increased *pari passu*, and therefore more glucose is presented to the tubules per minute, until ultimately there comes a time when the tubules are loaded to capacity and some glucose escapes reabsorption and is excreted in the urine. Analysis of this phenomenon in the dog has been made by Shannon and Fisher[49] and Shannon, Farber and Troast,[48] and shows that the tubules are capable of reabsorbing all the glucose from the glomerular filtrate up to a point where this reabsorption reaches a certain maximal rate, in milligrams of glucose per minute. For brevity we may designate this maximal rate of tubular reabsorption of glucose as glucose-Tm. Recent observations on man indicate that here precisely the same type of limitation applies; the maximal rate of tubular reabsorption of glucose in man typically ranges around 375 mgm. per minute.[56] This figure is easily determined by raising the plasma glucose to a high level, and measuring the simultaneous rate of filtration and of glucose excretion. The curve in Figure 3 represents the glucose clearance in an individual whose filtration rate (inulin clearance) is taken to be 125 c.c. per minute, whose maximal rate of tubular reabsorption of glucose (glucose Tm) is taken to be 320 mgm. per minute, and in whom the plasma level of glucose has been raised from 200 to 800 mgm. per cent. At 256 mgm. per cent of glucose in the plasma the rate of filtration of glucose (125 × 256/100 or 320 mgm. of glucose per minute) is just equal to the maximal rate of reabsorption; at plasma levels above this all excess glucose is excreted in the urine, so that the glucose clearance now rises and approaches the inulin clearance asymptotically. Thus the physiological basis of the glucose threshold consists of a constant maximal rate of tubular reabsorption combined with a variable rate of glomerular filtration and of course a variable concentration of glucose in the plasma and therefore in the glomerular filtrate.

Ralli, Friedman and Rubin[32] have shown that vitamin C is handled by the human kidney in a manner similar to glucose; the maximal rate of tubular reabsorption averages 2.2 mgm. per minute, which figure we have used in the chart; at a filtration rate of 125 cc. per minute, vitamin C will first appear in the urine at 1.76 mgm. per cent, and at increasing plasma levels the vitamin C clearance will increase and approach the inulin clearance asymptotically, as in the case of glucose.

SO_4,[16] PO_4,[17] hemoglobin,[29] and certain amino acids,[9] are reabsorbed by the tubules, and here apparently a similar limitation in the form of a maximal rate of tubular reabsorption applies. The situation is more complex in the case of Na and Cl,[47] but whether the tubular limitation is simple or complex, it is clear that the relations between load and capacity in respect to tubular activity cannot be overlooked in appraising any aspect of renal function.

Turning now to the process of tubular excretion, the fact that creatinine, phenol red, diodrast and other substances are excreted by the tubules does not exclude them from excretion by the glomeruli. They must be present in the glomerular filtrate in the same concentration as they are present in the filterable form (i.e. not bound to plasma proteins) per cc. of plasma water. The creatinine clearance, for example, has a value about 40 per cent greater than the inulin clearance; since creatinine is completely filterable from the plasma, this means that in addition to some 125 cc. of plasma per minute which are cleared of creatinine by filtration, an additional 50 cc. per minute are cleared by tubular excretion. Raising the plasma level of creatinine will not affect the filtration clearance, but it will affect the tubular clearance, for again there is a maximal quantity of creatinine which can be handled by the tubule cells per unit time. The net consequence of this circumstance is that at high plasma levels of creatinine the total creatinine clearance is depressed towards the level of the inulin clearance.[40] The same is true of phenol red[15] and diodrast, hippuran and iopax.[58, 60] In every instance where an adequate examination has been possible, it has been shown that, just as in the case of tubular reabsorption, so in tubular excretion there exists a limitation in tubular activity, which, at least as a first approximation, takes the form of a maximal rate of excretion.*

When the plasma concentration of any of these substances is raised above a critical level the tubular mechanism becomes saturated, so to speak, and excretes the substance at a maximal rate. This maximal rate has, of course, a different value for each substance. Again we may designate the maximal rate by Tm, and speak of the creatinine Tm, phenol red Tm, diodrast Tm, etc., and

---

* The glomerular excretion of all these substances, with the exception of creatinine, is complicated by the circumstance that they are in part bound to plasma proteins in apparently all species and are not completely filterable. Data are available for correcting for this protein binding in the case of a few substances.[53, 61]

these values will of course differ in different individuals, depending upon the quantity of tubular tissue participating in the excretory process. The maximal rate of tubular excretion is determined by deducting the quantity filtered through the glomeruli from the total quantity excreted per minute, when the plasma concentration has been raised to such a level as to load the tubule cells to full capacity. The curves shown in Figure 3 relating the creatinine, phenol red and diodrast clearances to plasma concentration, are calculated on the basis of typical Tm values in normal man.

The above discussion focusses attention again on the importance of accurately measuring the rate of glomerular filtration, for all subordinate calculations as to what is going on in the tubules in health or disease depend upon the accuracy of this measurement. For this reason I would like to return for a moment to the discussion of the inulin clearance. The difficulties presented in the exploration of renal function consist chiefly of the difficulties in obtaining substances for which accurate methods of analysis in blood and urine are available, and in the selection of substances which have suitable physiological properties. The field is narrowed by the fact that the renal tubules are known to reabsorb or excrete so many different types of compounds. Strong electrolytes are handled by the tubules in a complex manner, and many weak electrolytes presumably become entangled in these tubular processes or are themselves handled by specific reactions. Even though a weak electrolyte might escape tubular reabsorption or excretion in the normal kidney, or under special circumstances, there is no assurance that it would remain inviolable under all circumstances, or in the nephron with perturbed function. It is for this reason that the supplementary evidence available at this time on the use of inulin for measuring the filtration rate consists of a comparison of clearances under a variety of conditions.

Shannon has shown that in the dog[45] and man (unpublished) during hyperglycemia, when the glucose reabsorptive mechanism is loaded to capacity, xylose is excluded from tubular reabsorption, and the xylose clearance rises to identity with the inulin clearance. Consequently, as illustrated in Figure 4, during hyperglycemia we may equate the clearances of xylose, mannitol, sorbitol and inulin.

It has long been known that the drug phlorizin induces glycosuria at all plasma levels, and in our first studies we attributed this to the blocking of the reabsorption of glucose in the tubules.[20, 21] When phlorizin is administered to dog or man the process of sugar reabsorption by the tubules is completely abolished so that not only the glucose but also the xylose and sucrose clearances are nearly or quite identical with the inulin clearance,[6, 51] and, prior to direct examination, we may anticipate that after phlorizin this identity will include sorbitol and mannitol.

At high plasma levels of creatinine, the creatinine clearance approaches to within a few per cent of the inulin clearance, indicating that the inulin clearance is at the level of filtration. While Ralli, Friedman and Rubin's[32] demonstration that the vitamin C clearance rises from zero and approaches to within 10 per cent of the inulin clearance at high vitamin C levels is additional evidence in this direction.

Phlorizin depresses the tubular excretion of creatinine in lower animals where this process is highly developed,[46] and in man it entirely abolishes the normal difference between the creatinine and inulin clearances, a result which, in view of the above evidence, we must attribute to the depression of tubular activity.

These facts reaffirm the conviction that the inulin clearance is at the level of glomerular filtration in the human kidney.

Returning now to the process of tubular excretion (Figure 3) it will be observed, first, that the blood is cleared of substances such as phenol red and diodrast most efficiently at low levels, where the tubules are not loaded to capacity. Second, it is evident that diodrast is cleared more efficiently than is phenol red. In relation to this second point there must be an upper limit to the possible range of clearance values, for the kidneys cannot excrete more of any substance per unit time than is carried to them by the blood in that interval:* that is, the upper limit

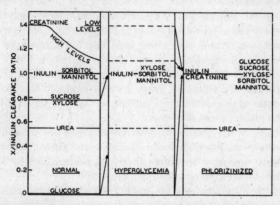

FIGURE 4. Diagrammatic summary of the present evidence, based on clearance ratios, indicating that the inulin clearance is at the level of glomerular filtration in man.

of renal clearance values will be that of a substance which is completely cleared from the blood, and this clearance will be identical with the rate at which blood (or plasma) is circulating through the kidneys.[15, 58,] †

This can be made clear by a simple example: if X is a substance which is completely cleared from the renal plasma in a single circulation through the kidneys, and if each cc. of arterial plasma (= systemic venous plasma) contains 1 mgm. of X and if 700 mgm. of X are being concurrently excreted in the urine each minute, it follows that 700 cc. of plasma, no more and no less, must be flowing through the kidneys in each minute's time. It is the simple problem of how many cc. of plasma are required to deliver 700 mgm. of X per minute, if each cc. of plasma carries 1 mgm.

* Excluding, of course, storage or synthesis in the renal parenchyma. Synthesis of phenol red, diodrast, etc. is clearly excluded, and storage of these compounds under standard conditions has been ruled out.[58]

† Because of greater ease of chemical determination, p-aminohippuric acid is recommended for measuring the effective renal plasma flow, instead of diodrast (11 and unpublished observations on dog and man).

The determination of the extent to which the clearance of any substance approaches completeness (i.e., 100 per cent extraction, as shown at the right of Figure 3) can only be answered by direct comparison of blood from the renal artery and the renal vein; and these blood samples must be collected under such conditions that renal function is not seriously disturbed. Since anesthesia and handling of the kidney do disturb renal function, the problem of the efficiency of renal extraction has been studied in dogs with one or both kidneys explanted under the skin so that blood can be drawn from the renal vein without serious disturbance to the animal. By this method White obtained for diodrast an average extraction ratio of 74 per cent, while Corcoran, Smith and Page[8] obtained an average value of 87 per cent. When allowance is made for the fact that some blood must pass directly through the renal capsule, some connective tissue, a few arteriovenous anastomoses or other paths wherein it is never exposed to excretory tissue, these figures indicate that the extraction ratio from such blood as is exposed to excretory tissue is probably close to 100 per cent. Moreover, the plasma diodrast clearance in normal man under basal conditions averages about 700 cc. per minute, which corresponds to about 1200 cc. of whole blood.[56] The basal cardiac output under these conditions is probably about 5000 cc. per minute. In short, the renal blood flow as given by the diodrast clearance constitutes about one quarter of the total cardiac output, so that the actual total renal blood flow cannot be much in excess of this.

We have, then, in the plasma diodrast clearance at low plasma levels of diodrast, a measure of the physiologically effective renal plasma flow in cc. per minute.* It is only necessary to divide the renal plasma flow by the percent of plasma in whole blood to obtain the renal blood flow.

By dividing the filtration rate (= inulin clearance) by the renal plasma flow (= diodrast clearance) we can calculate the fraction of the plasma which is filtered through the glomeruli. This filtration fraction will depend upon systemic blood pressure, the state of constriction or dilatation of the glomerular arterioles, the permeability of the glomerular capillaries, the intrarenal or capsular pressure, perhaps upon the time of contact of the blood with the glomerular capillaries, and possibly upon other factors. By following the filtration fraction under a variety of conditions we can learn much about the activity of the glomerular apparatus.

It will be convenient at this point to relate these quantitative methods to the architecture of the kidney, as illustrated in Figure 5. It will be recalled that in each kidney there are over a million nephrons, each of which is capable in theory

---

* The diodrast clearance as a measure of *total* renal blood flow is valid only so long as the extraction ratio does not change. If the extraction ratio falls, as it probably will in disease or renal anoxia, some blood will no longer be cleared by the tubular excretion of diodrast; and obviously one cannot measure uncleared blood by the clearance method. Under these conditions, however, residual, active tubular cells may be expected to clear such blood as is presented to them, and hence the diodrast clearance will still be a measure of the blood flow to this active tubular tissue. Hence the diodrast clearance is best identified as a measure of the 'effective renal blood flow.' For a discussion of the limitations of the clearance methods in the study of the diseased kidney see Smith.[55]

of functioning more or less independently. We may assume *a priori* that the blood flow to any nephron can be varied by physiological means, and that at a given blood flow the quantity of filtrate separated at the glomerulus can be varied by local changes in intraglomerular pressure, due, among other things, to changes in afferent and efferent arteriolar tone. It is conceivable that a glomerulus may be completely cut out of the circulation by local vasoconstriction, while the appended tubule continues to function in various excretory operations in the manner of the normal aglomerular nephron; or that blood can be shunted away from both glomerulus and tubule, rendering the entire nephron inactive. And conceivably the destruction of glomeruli or tubules may be effected separately during the course of disease.

It will simplify discussion if we define in terms of the physiology of the individual nephron the chief deviations from normal function which may be expected to occur

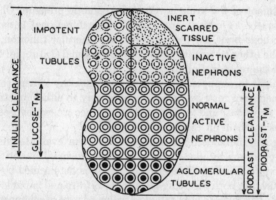

FIGURE 5. Functional types of nephrons to be expected in the normal and diseased kidney

1. We will designate as *normal active nephrons* those nephrons which possess both normal glomeruli and tubules.

2. The term, *aglomerular tubules* may be used to designate nephrons in which the glomeruli have ceased to function for any reason, but in which the tubule is functionally intact and receiving an adequate supply of blood, and is capable of carrying on excretory operations.

3. Any nephrons which, though potentially capable of normal function, are excluded from function by ischemia we will designate as *inactive nephrons*.

4. The terms *impotent tubules* we can apply to nephrons in which the glomerulus remains intact and active, but the tubule, by virtue of ischemia or local intracellular damage, is incapable of function. This category would include only patent nephrons which are connected with the collecting ducts and which therefore serve as passive conduits to drain glomerular filtrate out of the body. This category is important in the diseased kidney where the tubules may lose their excretory activity, without losing their reabsorptive activity or without

becoming detached from the glomerulus or collecting duct. The blood presented to such nephrons may escape uncleared, although it is likely that some of it will be cleared by adjacent normal nephrons. If such blood escapes uncleared, a proportional reduction in over-all extraction ratio must occur. Impotent nephrons as here defined are particularly in evidence in hypertensive disease.[56]

5. In the category of inert scarred tissue we would include not only fibrotic glomeruli and fragmented or necrotic tubular tissue, but also anatomically intact nephrons which are obstructed by casts of epithelium, albumin, etc., or which are disconnected from the collecting ducts, so that function is impossible.

In the above schema the nephron is viewed as a unitary structure with but a single function. This is of course not true; the proximal tubule is probably concerned with the reabsorption of sodium, chloride, glucose, vitamin C and possibly other constituents of the glomerular filtrate, and with the excretion of creatinine, phenol red, diodrast and possibly other substances. The thin segment is perhaps chiefly concerned with the reabsorption of water, the distal segment with the final adjustment of the urine in respect to osmotic pressure, Cl, pH, HCO_3, etc. But obviously we cannot appraise all these functional activities at this time. Our methods limit our examination to glomerular function, on the one hand, and on the other to two functions of the proximal (?) tubule: the excretion of diodrast and the reabsorption of glucose.

A priori it might be supposed that even in the healthy kidney the number of normal active nephrons may be variable, giving way to either inactive nephrons or aglomerular nephrons; and with greater confidence we can expect to discover such transitions to occur in consequence of disease.

But utilizing the methods discussed above, we can evaluate the number of normal active nephrons by glucose-Tm, since the maximal quantity of glucose in mgm. per minute which the kidneys will absorb is determined by the number of nephrons which are both receiving glomerular filtrate and capable of reabsorbing glucose from this filtrate. If the glomerulus of a particular nephron closes, converting it to an aglomerular tubule, or if the tubule itself is rendered inactive by ischemia, it will cease to contribute to glucose-Tm, and this figure will be decreased accordingly. Glucose-Tm will also be decreased by destruction of the reabsorptive capacity of the tubule, even though the glomeruli remain open. Though it is impossible at present to distinguish which of these three causes— glomerular ischemia, tubular ischemia or tubular injury—may be responsible for reducing glucose-Tm in the diseased kidney, this measurement can be used to determine whether the number of active normal nephrons in the kidney of a particular individual can be increased or decreased by any method.

Diodrast-Tm serves to measure the number of active excretory tubules, whether glomerular or aglomerular; it affords therefore a measurement of the total quantity of intact, tubular excretory tissue in the kidney, which may be designated as the tubular excretory mass.[58] We infer that this tubular excretory mass is identical with the quantity of physiologically intact proximal tubular tissue, since the evidence indicates that it is only by the proximal tubule that diodrast is excreted. Within wide limits both glucose-Tm and diodrast-Tm will, under appropriate plasma concentrations of glucose and diodrast, be independent of the rate of filtration or the rate of blood flow. That is, they afford absolute measurements of the mass of functioning tissue.*

Except insofar as glucose reabsorption and diodrast excretion may be separately impaired by disease, the relative values of glucose-Tm and diodrast-Tm, as compared with the normal ratio, will afford an indication of the presence and approximate number of aglomerular nephrons in the kidney.

Glomerular filtration can occur in both normal active nephrons and in the glomeruli of impotent tubules (which by definition are still connected with functional glomeruli); again the fraction of the glomerular filtrate furnished by these two adjacent categories cannot be distinguished directly, but in principle it should be possible to estimate the number of impotent tubules on the basis of the relative values of the filtration rate and glucose-Tm or diodrast-Tm.

Inactive tubules will be revealed only indirectly by an increase in diodrast-Tm under experimental or therapeutic conditions which abolish tubular ischemia, just as inactive glomeruli will be revealed only indirectly by an increase in glucose-Tm under conditions whereby glomerular ischemia is abolished.

Inert scarred tissue can be evaluated only by presumption when glucose or diodrast Tm are decreased below standard normal values.

By slowing raising the plasma level of glucose, the rate of filtration in various glomeruli, relative to the glucose reabsorptive capacity of the attached tubule, can be determined.

Similarly, by slowly raising the plasma level of diodrast, the rate of perfusion of the tubular tissue, relative to the excretory capacity of the involved tubule cells, can be determined.

These two 'titration' methods have been applied to the normal human kidney and have shown that there are no inactive glomeruli or tubules; indeed, both glomerular activity and tubular perfusion are remarkably uniform throughout the renal parenchyma. In disease, however, the pattern of physiological activity may be markedly modified.[56] In the frog[13] the number of active glomeruli increase more or less in proportion to the urine flow, revealing what is perhaps a marked difference in renal regulation between cold-blooded animals and mammals. It is to be noted that the former possess a renal-portal circulation which can maintain the tubules during periods of widespread glomerular inactivity, whereas the latter do not.

---

* Short of complete cessation of filtration, the degree of reduction in filtration rate necessary to cause an individual nephron to drop out of glucose-Tm will be determined by the plasma level of glucose, which fact must be taken into account in the definition of 'normal active nephrons.'

Similarly, the degree of reduction in blood flow necessary to cause an individual nephron to drop out of diodrast-Tm will be determined by the plasma level of diodrast, which fact must be taken into account in the definition of the tubular excretory mass.

The diodrast clearance affords no information on the blood flow to either impotent tubules or scar tissue, but only to intact tubular tissue (the tubular excretory mass); hence it is appropriate for purposes of physiological comparison to relate the diodrast clearance to diodrast-Tm.

To discuss these matters further would, however, take us beyond the purpose of this lecture, which is to set forth briefly the methods and underlying principles for the study of renal function, rather than to describe in detail their practical application.

REFERENCES

1. Book, M. H., The secreting area of the glomerus. J. Anat., 71: 91, 1936.
2. Bott, P. A., and Richards, A. N., The passage of protein molecules through the glomerular membranes. J. Biol. Chem., 141: 291, 1941.
3. Bunim, J. J., Smith, W. W., and Smith, H. W., The diffusion coefficient of inulin and other substances of interest in renal physiology. J. Biol. Chem., 118: 667, 1937.
4. Cameron, G., and Chambers, R., Direct evidence of function in kidney of an early human fetus. Am. J. Physiol., 123: 482, 1938.
5. Chambers, R., and Kempton, R. T., Indications of function of the chick mesonephros in tissue culture with phenol red. J. Cell. and Comp. Physiol., 3: 131, 1933.
6. Chasis, H., Jolliffe, N., and Smith, H. W., Action of phlorizin on excretion of glucose, xylose, sucrose, creatinine and urea by man. J. Clin. Invest., 12: 1083, 1933.
7. Chasis, H., and Smith, H. W., The excretion of urea in normal man and in subjects with glomerulonephritis. J. Clin. Invest., 17: 347, 1938.
8. Corcoran, A. C., Smith, H. W., and Page, I. H., The removal of diodrast from blood by the dog's explanted kidney. Am. J. Physiol., 134: 333, 1941.
9. Doty, J. R., Reabsorption of certain amino acids and derivatives by the kidney tubules. Proc. Soc. Exper. Biol. & Med., 46: 129, 1941.
10. Elsom, K. A., Bott, P. A., and Shiels, E. H., On the excretion of skiodan, diodrast and hippuran by the dog. Am. J. Physiol., 115: 548, 1936.
11. Finkelstein, N., Aliminosa, L. M., and Smith, H. W., The renal clearances of hippuric acid and pyridone derivatives. Am. J. Physiol., 133: 276, 1941.
12. Forster, R. P., The use of inulin and creatinine as glomerular filtrate measuring substances in the frog. J. Cell. and Comp. Physiol., 12: 213, 1938.
13. Forster, R. P., The nature of the glucose reabsorptive process in the frog renal tubule. Evidence for intermittency of glomerular function in the intact animal. J. Cell. and Comp. Physiol., 20: 55, 1942.
14. Friedman, G. J., Sherry, S., and Ralli, E. P., The mechanism of the excretion of vitamin C by the human kidney at low and normal plasma levels of ascorbic acid. J. Clin. Invest., 19: 685, 1940.
15. Goldring, W., Clarke, R. W., and Smith, H. W., Phenol red clearance in normal man. J. Clin. Invest., 15: 221, 1936.
16. Goudsmit, A., Jr., and Keith, N. M., Relative significance of concentration of inorganic sulfate in the serum and of its renal clearance. Arch. Int. Med., 66: 816, 1940.
17. Harrison, H. E., and Harrison, H. C., The renal excretion of inorganic phosphate in relation to the action of vitamin D and parathyroid hormone. J. Clin. Invest., 20: 47, 1941.
18. Hendrix, J. P., Westfall, B. B., and Richards, A. N., Quantitative studies of the composition of glomerular urine. XIV. The glomerular excretion of inulin in frogs and necturi. J. Biol. Chem., 116: 735, 1936.
19. Höber, R., Über die Harnbildung in der Froschniere; über die Auscheidung des Harnstoffs. Arch. f. d. ges. Physiol., 224: 422, 1930.
20. Jolliffe, N., Shannon, J. A., and Smith, H. W., Excretion of urine in dog; use of non-metabolized sugars in measurement of glomerular filtrate. Am. J. Physiol., 100: 301, 1932.
21. Jolliffe, N., Shannon, J. A., and Smith, H. W., Excretion of urine in dog; effects of xylose and sucrose upon glomerular and urea clearances. Am. J. Physiol., 101: 639, 1932.

22. KAPLAN, B. I., AND SMITH, H. W., Excretion of inulin, creatinine, xylose and urea in the normal rabbit. Am. J. Physiol., 113: 354, 1935.

23. LANDIS, E. M., ELSOM, K. A., BOTT, P. A., AND SHIELS, E. H., Simultaneous plasma clearances of creatinine and certain organic compounds of iodine in relation to human kidney function. J. Clin. Invest., 15: 397, 1936.

24. McCANCE, R. A., AND WIDDOWSON, E. M., Functional disorganization of the kidney in disease. J. Physiol., 95: 36, 1939.

25. MARSHALL, E. K., JR., The comparative physiology of the kidney in relation to theories of renal secretion. Physiol. Rev., 14: 133, 1934.

26. MILLER, B. F., ALVING, A. S., AND RUBIN, J., The renal excretion of inulin at low plasma concentrations of this compound, and its relationship to the glomerular filtration rate in normal, nephritic and hypertensive individuals. J. Clin. Invest., 19: 89, 1940.

27. MILLER, B., AND WINKLER, A. W., The renal excretion of endogenous creatinine in man. Comparison with exogenous creatinine and inulin. J. Clin. Invest., 17: 31, 1938.

28. MÖLLER, E., McINTOSH, J. F., AND VAN SLYKE, D. D., Studies of urea excretion: II. Relationship between urine volume and the rate of urea excretion by normal adults. J. Clin. Invest., 6: 427, 1928.

29. MONKE, J. V., AND YUILE, C. L., The renal clearance of hemoglobin in the dog. J. Exper. Med., 72: 149, 1940.

30. MORITZ, A. R., AND HAYMAN, J. M., JR., The disappearance of glomeruli in chronic kidney disease. Am. J. Path., 10: 505, 1934.

31. PITTS, R. F., The excretion of creatine and creatinine in teleost, *Epinephelus morio*. Carnegie Institute of Washington, Year Book No. 35, 1936.

32. RALLI, E. P., FRIEDMAN, G. J., AND RUBIN, S. H., The mechanism of the excretion of vitamin C by the human kidney. J. Clin. Invest., 17: 765, 1938.

33. REHBERG, P. B., Studies on kidney function. I. The rate of filtration and reabsorption in the human kidney. Biochem. J., 20: 447, 1926.

34. RICHARDS, A. N., Urine formation in the amphibian kidney. The Harvey Lectures, 1934–35.

35. RICHARDS, A. N., Processes of urine formation. Proc. Roy. Soc., London Series B, 126: 398, 1938.

36. RICHARDS, A. N., Physiology of the kidney. Carpenter Lecture, Bulletin of the N. Y. Acad. of Med., 14, 2nd series, 1938.

37. RICHARDS, A. N., BOTT, P. A., AND WESTFALL, B. B., Experiments concerning the possibility that inulin is secreted by the renal tubules. Am. J. Physiol., 123: 281, 1938.

38. RICHARDS, A. N., WESTFALL, B. B., AND BOTT, P. A., Inulin and creatinine clearances in dogs, with notes on some late effects of uranium poisoning. J. Biol. Chem., 116: 749, 1936.

39. SHANNON, J. A., The excretion of inulin by the dogfish, Squalus acanthus. J. Cell. and Comp. Physiol., 5: 301, 1934:

40. SHANNON, J. A., The renal excretion of creatinine in man J. Clin. Invest., 14: 403, 1935.

41. SHANNON, J. A., The excretion of inulin by the dog. Am. J. Physiol., 112: 405, 1935.

42. SHANNON, J. A., The excretion of inulin and creatinine at low urine flows by the normal dog. Am. J. Physiol., 114: 362, 1936.

43. SHANNON, J. A., Excretion of inulin, creatinine, xylose and urea in the sheep. Proc. Soc. Exper. Biol. and Med., 37: 379, 1937.

44. SHANNON, J. A., The excretion of exogenous creatinine by the chicken. J. Cell. and Comp. Physiol., 11: 123, 1938.

45. SHANNON, J. A., Tubular reabsorption of xylose in normal dog. Am. J. Physiol., 122: 775, 1938.

46. SHANNON, J. A., Renal tubular excretion. Physiol. Rev., 19: 63, 1939.

47. SHANNON, J. A., The control of the renal excretion of water. I. The effect of variations in the state of hydration on water excretion in dogs with diabetes insipidus.
J. Exper. Med., 76: 371, 1942.

48. SHANNON, J. A., FARBER, S., AND TROAST, L., The measurement of glucose Tm in the
normal dog. Am. J. Physiol., 133: 752, 1941.

49. SHANNON, J. A., AND FISHER, S., The renal tubular reabsorption of glucose in the normal
dog. Am. J. Physiol., 122: 765, 1938.

50. SHANNON, J. A., AND RANGES, H. A., On the renal tubular excretion of creatinine in
normal man. J. Clin. Invest., 20: 169, 1941.

51. SHANNON, J. A., AND SMITH, H. W., The excretion of inulin, xylose and urea by normal
and phlorizinized man. J. Clin. Invest., 14: 393, 1935.

52. SMITH, H. W., The composition of urine in the seal. J. Cell. and Comp. Physiol.,
7: 465, 1936.

53. SMITH, H. W., The Physiology of the Kidney. Oxford University Press. 1937.

54. SMITH, H. W., The Physiology of the Renal Circulation. The Harvey Lectures, 35:
166, 1939.

55. SMITH, H. W., Note on the interpretations of clearance methods in the diseased kidney.
J. Clin. Invest., 20: 631, 1941.

56. SMITH, H. W., I. Renal Physiology Between Two Wars. J. Mt. Sinai Hospital. William Henry Welch Lectures, 41, 1943.
SMITH, H. W., II. The Application of Saturation Methods to the Study of Glomerular
and Tubular Function in the Human Kidney. Ibid., 59, 1943.

57. SMITH, H. W., AND CLARKE, R. W., The excretion of inulin and creatinine by the anthropoid apes and other infrahuman primates. Am. J. Physiol., 122: 132, 1938.

58. SMITH, H. W., GOLDRING, W., AND CHASIS, H., The measurement of the tubular excretory mass, effective blood flow and filtration rate in the normal human kidney.
J. Clin. Invest., 17: 263, 1938.

59. SMITH, W. W., FINKELSTEIN, N., AND SMITH, H. W., Renal excretion of hexitols (sorbitol, mannitol, and dulcitol) and their derivatives (sorbitan, isomannide, and
sorbide) and of endogenous creatinine-like chromogen in dog and man. J. Biol.
Chem., 135: 231, 1940.

60. SMITH, W. W., AND RANGES, H. A., Renal clearances of iopax, neoiopax and skiodan
in man. Am. J. Physiol., 123: 720, 1938.

61. SMITH, W. W., AND SMITH, H. W., Protein binding of phenol red, diodrast and other
substances in plasma. J. Biol. Chem., 124: 107, 1938.

62. STEINITZ, K., The renal excretion of sucrose in normal man; comparison with inulin.
Am. J. Physiol., 129: 252, 1940.

63. VAN SLYKE, D. D., HILLER, A., AND MILLER, B. F., The distribution of ferrocyanide,
inulin, creatinine, and urea in the blood and its effect on the significance of their
extraction percentages. Am. J. Physiol., 113: 629, 1935.

64. WESTFALL, B. B., AND LANDIS, E. M., The molecular weight of inulin. J. Biol. Chem.,
116: 727, 1936.

65. WHITE, H. L., Observations on the behavior of diodrast in the dog. Am. J. Physiol.,
130: 454, 1940.

THE RENAL BLOOD FLOW IN NORMAL SUBJECTS

THE RENAL BLOOD FLOW IN NORMAL SUBJECTS

It is appropriate to apply the methods which have been described in the previous lecture in a few experiments that throw light upon the physiological control of the renal blood flow.

The first experiment which I would like to discuss concerns the effects of oil of juniper on renal function (Figure 1). Many years ago oil of juniper enjoyed a vogue as a diuretic, which fact led us to suspect that it might have some action on the renal circulation. (The experiment serves chiefly to illustrate the method of examination.) The subject was prepared for the determination of renal clearances in the usual manner. He was well hydrated by the copious administration of water, both the night before and early in the morning of the examination, in order to establish good urine flows. Suitable plasma concentrations of diodrast and inulin were maintained by continuous intravenous infusion, and urine was collected by catheter, the bladder being rinsed out with saline at the end of each urine collection period. The data recorded in the figure are the cc. of plasma cleared per minute of diodrast (D) and inulin (IN), the filtration fraction (FF), the brachial blood pressure, and, at the bottom, the urine flow in cc. per minute (V). The diodrast clearance indicates the renal plasma flow, the inulin clearance the rate of glomerular filtration, the filtration fraction the per cent of plasma filtered through the glomeruli.

As shown by the three control periods at the left of the chart, he had a basal renal plasma flow averaging 782 cc. per minute. The administration of 1 cc. oil of juniper had no effect on either the renal plasma flow or the filtration rate. The urine flow (V) increased transiently from slightly above 1 cc. to above 8 cc. per minute; whether this diuresis is attributable to local action of the oil of juniper upon the renal tubules, or to a reduction in the secretion of the antidiuretic hormone of the posterior pituitary gland in consequence of reflex excitation from the gastrointestinal tract, is undetermined, though the latter seems the more likely explanation. The phenomenon of diuresis is, however, of secondary importance; changes in urine flow represent merely slight changes in the reabsorption of water from the glomerular filtrate, and since such changes can be elicited by many different types of stimuli acting through the supraoptic-hypophyseal mechanism, they have little fundamental significance with regard to renal function. What we were looking for when we did this experiment was a change in renal plasma flow, but in this respect the experiment was entirely negative. The slight parallel variations in the diodrast and inulin clearances are probably not real fluctuations in activity but errors due to incomplete emptying of the bladder.

We have in our records a considerable number of such negative experiments, for we have had occasion to examine the action of a number of drugs upon renal function in our search for certain desired effects, and usually this has been the result. But these negative experiments at least enable us to say that the renal plasma flow and filtration rate in a normal individual can be expected to remain quite constant over a two or three hour interval, or for that matter, in repeated examination at widely separated intervals. One subject examined in the basal condition on 12 occasions over a period of 4 months has shown an extreme variation of only ± 15 per cent from the average figure. Assuming a constant basal or resting blood pressure, this fact merely bespeaks the stability of the vascular bed of the kidneys.

We may go farther than emphasizing the constancy of the renal blood flow in any one individual: it is in fact quite uniform in different individuals. In comparing 61 normal men whom we have examined in the basal condition,

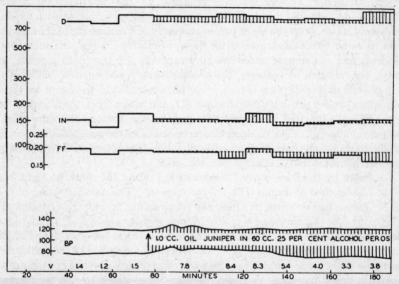

FIGURE 1. Action of oil of juniper on effective renal plasma flow (D = diodrast clearance in cc. per minute), filtration rate (IN = inulin clearance in cc. per minute), filtration fraction (FF = inulin/diodrast clearance ratio), blood pressure (BP in mm. Hg) and urine flow (V in cc. per minute). (From 4.)

the standard deviation, counting each individual but once, is 19.5 per cent of the mean. The mean value is 697 cc. of plasma, or 1209 cc. of whole blood per minute, which is about one-quarter of the cardiac output under these conditions.[16] Though this uniformity in renal blood flow is not wholly unexpected on an anatomical and physiological basis, the absolute magnitude of 1200 cc. is rather surprising. It is, however, in agreement with observations on anesthetized animals.

Were I to tax your patience by showing a fair sample of our negative experiments, such as the one given in Figure 1, you would be prepared to believe, as indeed we were once tempted to believe, that the renal circulation and the glomerular apparatus are so constructed as to be incapable of variation. So I pass immediately to the demonstration that the renal circulation can be profoundly altered, and I have selected for this demonstration the action of that dynamic hormone, adrenalin (Figure 2). The subject of this experiment showed in four control periods an average renal plasma flow of 926 cc. per minute. Adrenalin (0.5 mgm. intramuscularly and 0.5 mgm. subcutaneously) reduced the plasma flow to a minimum of 510 cc. (i.e., to 55 per cent of the control value) and, in view of the fact that the mean brachial blood pressure was not lowered, it must be concluded that this reduction in renal plasma flow was due to constriction of the arterioles of the kidney, either on the afferent or efferent side of the glomeruli. The locus of the constriction can, we believe, be identified

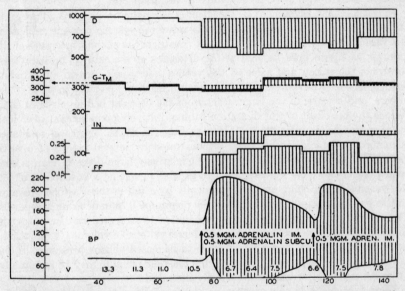

FIGURE 2. Action of adrenalin on effective renal plasma flow, etc. Legend as in Figure 1. G-Tm = maximal rate of tubular reabsorption of glucose under conditions of tubular saturation, in mgm. per minute. G-Tm is indirect index of the number of active glomeruli in the kidney.

from the available data. Had the afferent arterioles been constricted the glomerular pressure would have been reduced, and consequently the filtration fraction would have fallen, while efferent constriction would have raised the glomerular pressure and increased the filtration fraction. The fact that the filtration fraction rose rather than fell is therefore evidence that it was the efferent rather than the afferent arterioles which were constricted. This experiment on man confirms, then, the 'paradoxical' action of adrenalin as demonstrated many years ago in the frog kidney by Richards and Plant. Since the filtration fraction increased almost in the same proportion as the plasma flow was reduced, the filtration rate remained almost unchanged; and had we observed the filtration rate alone we might have concluded that adrenalin had no effect upon the kidney. Here we have a demonstration of an important fact about the glomerular circulation. The construction of the glomeruli is such that when the renal blood flow is altered in consequence of changes in efferent arteriolar tone, the simultaneous and opposite changes in glomerular pressure tend to maintain the filtration rate at a constant level. The filtration rate in normal man is remarkably constant, even more constant than the renal blood flow; and this constancy may be attributed to the circumstance that changes in renal blood flow appear to be mediated by changes in the tone of the efferent, rather than the afferent, glomerular arterioles.[4] This unique feature of the glomerular apparatus is of considerable importance since extreme changes in renal blood flow may occur in the diseased kidney with very little change in filtration rate.

In passing, may I comment on the effect of adrenalin upon the blood pressure. It is still frequently stated that adrenalin raises the systolic pressure because it is a vasoconstrictor drug. Admittedly it constricts the efferent arterioles of the kidneys, as shown here, as well as the arterioles of the skin; it probably also constricts the spleen and some of the venous reservoirs. But in approximate doses it dilates the arterioles in the skeletal muscles and possibly in some of the viscera, and because of the larger fraction of the vascular bed involved in these regions the net effect of this dilatation is quantitatively preponderant over such vasoconstriction as may occur. Consequently the mean peripheral resistance is frequently *reduced*, as has been demonstrated by several groups of investigators.[3, 2, 18, 19] So far as the net effect of relatively large doses in man is concerned, adrenalin must be considered as generally exerting a vasodilator effect, this vasodilatation being evidenced typically by a fall in the diastolic pressure. In this particular experiment the diastolic pressure fell to undeterminable levels. The rise in systolic pressure must be attributed to increased cardiac output in consequence of increased heart rate and increased stroke volume, the increased stroke volume in part being attributable to increased venous pressure. If the cardiac output is sufficiently increased the diastolic pressure may be maintained at its control level or even momentarily increased.[3]

There is included in this experiment a series of measurements of glucose-Tm (G-Tm) obtained by maintaining the plasma glucose at 380–445 mgm. per cent. During the four control periods this value averaged 306 mgm. per minute; during the action of adrenalin it averaged 325 mgm. per minute, i.e., it increased by 6 per cent, an increase of doubtful significance. Had adrenalin closed any glomeruli by its vasoconstrictor action, this figure would necessarily have been reduced, regardless of any changes in the filtration rate in the remaining active nephrons. The failure of glucose-Tm to decrease shows that adrenalin in this dose (which is about the maximal dose which may be administered to man without serious disturbance) did not close any glomeruli.

We have examined a number of so-called sympaticomimetic drugs, but the only other one of immediate interest is ephedrine (Figure 3). The net effect of this drug, in man is, like that of adrenalin, vasodilatation, as evidenced by a decrease in the total peripheral resistance.[3] We have been rather surprised to find that ephedrine in therapeutic doses has no or a negligible effect upon the renal circulation, suggesting that the fundamental mode of action of adrenalin and ephedrine is quite different. (It is interesting in this connection to refer to a recent discussion of the action of ephedrine by Gaddum.[6]) Adrenalin, as I have pointed out above, acts apparently exclusively upon the efferent glomerular arteriole. We have found no drug which acts exclusively upon the afferent arteriole, though there is evidence that afferent constriction can be elicited by painful stimuli and other circumstances where reflex excitation is involved.

I turn now to experiments dealing with vasodilatation of the renal arterioles. Early in our investigations we sought some means of increasing the renal blood flow by vasodilatation and we have expended an extravagant amount of time on this problem. May I remark in this connection that when the experimenter

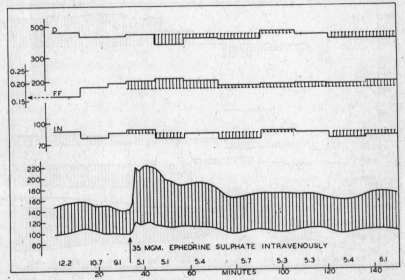

FIGURE 3. Action of ephedrine on effective renal plasma flow, etc. Legend as in Figure 1

fails to accomplish a result which is rationally to be expected he is likely to be on the threshold of a new discovery, and further, that he frequently learns more from accidental adventures than from well planned experiments. That we only hyperbolically found means of producing renal hyperemia in the human kidney involves, in a sense, a new discovery about that organ, and the discovery of the method of producing this hyperemia certainly rests upon a fortuitous circumstance.

Inulin, here used to measure the filtration rate, is physiologically inactive when properly prepared, as may be demonstrated by the absence of any disturbance in renal function, body temperature, blood pressure or subjective feeling, in subjects receiving intravenous infusions over periods of several hours. But early in our investigations we encountered difficulty in obtaining suitable inulin, inasmuch as some samples of it contain a powerful pyrogen, comparable to the pyrogen present in typhoid vaccine and probably comparable to the pyrogen that too frequently invades intravenous infusions of saline, glucose, etc. We do not yet know the nature of this pyrogen, but its source may be the fragmented bodies of contaminating yeast, mould or bacterial cells which have grown upon the inulin during the process of manufacture.[15]

In any case, we soon discovered that whenever the pyrogenic reaction, which consists of headache, lumbar pain, nausea and ultimate fever, was encountered renal hyperemia invariably occurred. This fact led us to investigate the action of typhoid vaccine. As shown in Figure 4, after a short latent period, which serves also as a 'control' period, both diastolic and systolic pressure typically

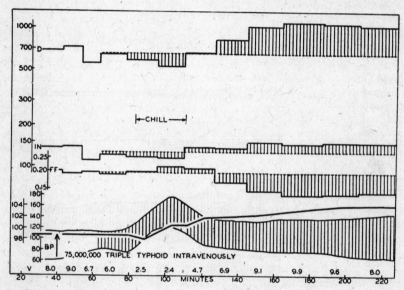

FIGURE 4. Illustrating the renal hyperemia produced by the pyrexial reaction. Legend as in Figure 1. Blood pressure was here taken by sphygmomanometer. (From 4.)

increase, this pressor phase usually coinciding with the febril chill. As the chill passes the blood pressure falls, the diastolic usually falling below its control level, indicating that dilatation has occurred some place in the arteriolar bed. During the pressor phase the renal plasma flow may be substantially reduced, but during the subsequent phase of reduced diastolic pressure the renal plasma flow increases again and mounts to values substantially above the control level. This renal hyperemia is accompanied by a decreased filtration fraction, indicating that it is a result of dilation of the efferent glomerular arterioles. The change in filtration fraction is usually such as to just offset the increase in plasma flow, so that the filtration rate remains almost unchanged. Again, were one observing only the filtration rate it might be inferred, quite erroneously, that no change had taken place in renal function.

After examining the effects of typhoid vaccine, we turned to a particular sample of highly pyrogenic inulin (No. 268) as affording a superior method for producing renal hyperemia in man. This particular sample of inulin will produce a marked renal hyperemia in doses of 50 mgm. intravenously.* In thus turning evil to good account, we are utilizing the only method known to us for inducing renal hyperemia, for no drug which we have tried has this effect.

After adequate doses of pyrogen an increase in renal plasma flow of 50 to 75 per cent can be expected, though we have seen in one subject whose basal plasma flow averaged 777 cc. per minute (= 1204 cc. of whole blood), a hyperemia amounting to 1894 cc. of plasma (= 3005 cc. of whole blood) per minute, an increase of 244 per cent.†

We have used the pyrogen method of producing renal hyperemia to examine the question of whether or not there are any inactive glomeruli or tubules in the normal or diseased kidney, and for this purpose it is desirable to prevent any rise in body temperature. This can be accomplished by the administration of amidopyrine prior to the administration of pyrogen. It was in this connection that we discovered that the amidopryine blocks not only the fever, but also the rise in blood pressure, the chill, the nausea, and usually all of the subjective symptoms, without blocking the renal hyperemia.

A comparison of the response of the same subject to pyrogenic inulin, with and without amidopyrine, has been given elsewhere,[13] and a more detailed study of the circulatory response under the quiet conditions obtaining after treatment with amidopyrine may be included here (Figure 5). Unlike the reaction elicited in the untreated subject, there is no chill or nausea, no vasoconstrictor phase in the blood pressure response, and no rise in body temperature. In the subject illustrated, renal hyperemia (C_D) began about 90 minutes after the injection of pyrogen, and perhaps had not reached its height at the conclusion of the observations. There was an initial decrease in renal plasma flow, a phenomenon rarely very marked in man but one which is usually quite evident in the dog[9] and seal[1] indicating that an initial vasoconstrictor phase may be an intrinsic part of the pyrogenic reaction. The filtration rate, after a moderate decrease, remained quite constant throughout the hyperemia.

The cardiac index (CI) increased significantly during the renal hyperemia, an increase attributable to a substantial increase in heart rate (HR) and a lesser increase in stroke volume (SV). The total peripheral resistance (R) decreased as the cardiac output increased, the resultant of the two terms giving a mean pressure which was well maintained until the last period. (Although in the experiment illustrated in Figure 5 the circulatory changes are of a minimal nature,

* This inulin is of course thoroughly sterilized by boiling before administration. The pyrogenic activity of this particular sample is in striking contrast to the fact that when completely non-pyrogenic as much as 100 grams of inulin may be given without renal or systemic disturbance.

† In more recent experiments it has been shown that the diodrast clearance and the p-aminohippuric acid clearance remain equal during pyrogenic hyperemia. Since p-aminohippuric acid does not penetrate the red cells in man *in vivo*, this fact excludes increased red-cell transportation as contributing to the observed increase in diodrast clearance.

as compared with other experiments given by the authors, this particular experiment is chosen for reproduction because the circulatory changes are qualitatively typical and uniform, and unmarred by the complication of excessive reduction in blood pressure or experimental interference.)

It is interesting to note that pyrexial hyperemia has been shown to occur, in both dog[9] and man[2], in the denervated as well is in the innervated kidney. Either the pyrogen reacts directly with the renal arterioles, or it causes the secre-

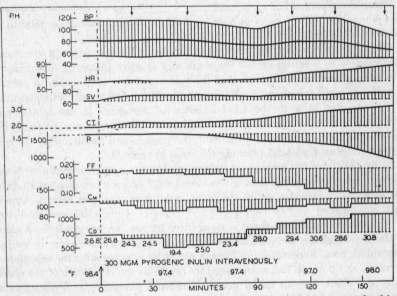

FIGURE 5. The renal and circulatory response to pyrogenic inulin in a normal subject premedicated with amidopyrine. BP = blood pressure in mm. Hg as recorded from the femoral artery by a Hamilton manometer, the thick line being the integrated mean pressure; HR = heart rate; SV = stroke volume in cc. as recorded by the ballistocardiograph; CI = cardiac index in liters per minute per sq. meter of body surface; R = peripheral resistance in dynes cm.$^{-5}$ sec.; C_M = mannitol clearance, substituted here for the inulin clearance; C_D = diodrast clearance; F = rectal temperature. The figures below C_D show the renal fraction, or that fraction of the total cardiac output going to the kidneys. (From 2.)

tion of some as yet unidentified vasodilator substance which affects these arterioles. An important problem remains here for investigation, for it may be that if the second interpretation is correct, the humoral agent is derived from the kidney itself.

The action of adrenalin and of pyrogen show that the renal blood flow can be decreased and increased through a considerable range, and it was our naive supposition that anesthetic section of the renal nerves would produce renal hyperemia by cutting off tonic vasoconstrictor impulses from the central nervous system. However, this expectation proved to be in error. In a series of investigations on normal subjects with high spinal anesthesia[17] it has been demonstrated that anesthesia adequate to block the reflex vasomotor responses has no significant effect upon the renal blood flow and we have concluded that when a subject is in the truly *basal* condition, i.e., horizontal and emotionally at ease, there are no tonic vasomotor impulses going to the kidney. The evidence points strongly to the conclusion that under these basal conditions the renal blood flow is regulated entirely by the autonomous or local activity of the renal arterioles.* This is not to deny, however, that the renal vasomotor nerves, like the rest of the sympathetic system, can be brought into action by multitudinous stimuli.

Indeed, it is easy to demonstrate that the renal arterioles are functionally connected with the nervous system. Elementary physiology teaches us that *Homo sapiens* pays a substantial price for his upright posture; every time he stands erect his blood tends to accumulate in the subcardial regions, particularly in the capillary and venous channels; he normally resists the venous failure which this stagnation favors by walking to and fro, the restless contractions of his leg muscles, aided by the venous valves, serving to promote the return of blood to the right heart. If, however, he stands still progressive venous stagnation leads to progressive decrease in cardiac output, which in turn tends to reduce arterial pressure; through the vaso-sensitive zones (aortic arch and carotid sinus) the first lowering of mean arterial pressure elicits reflex vasoconstriction throughout the body. In this response to posture we have one means of evoking reflex excitation of the renal vasoconstrictor paths.

In the experiment shown in Figure 6 the subject, after three control periods in the horizontal position, stood upright, leaning against the wall until syncope occurred. This is not a very protracted ordeal, as most of those who have tried it can testify. As soon as he assumed the upright posture the renal plasma flow decreased; in view of the fact that the mean arterial pressure did not decrease, but was in fact slightly increased, this renal ischemia must be attributed to constriction of the renal arterioles. The fall in filtration fraction indicates that here constriction of the afferent arterioles plays an important part. (Another experiment of this type, using the tilt table, is presented elsewhere[13].)

Again, in passing I would like to comment on a related aspect of this experiment. It is frequently stated that orthostatic syncope is caused by arteriolar dilatation following vasomotor failure. But you will notice that the blood pressure of the subject shown here gives no evidence of vasodilatation; rather he displays a picture of progressively decreasing venous return with consequent decreasing cardiac output, the arterioles seemingly remaining constricted to the end. Though we cannot assert that it is invariably true, syncope in this case was accompanied by a marked slowing of the heart, and we suspect that it is this cardiac inhibition, presumably mediated through the vagus, which is immediately

* This conclusion acquires special interest in view of recent anatomical studies of the glomerular apparatus which indicate the presence in both the afferent and efferent arterioles of a rather elaborate system of specialized myo-epithelioid cells the local responses of which may determine the caliber of these vessels (See 13).

responsible for cerebral anoxia and loss of consciousness. The importance of cardiac inhibition in syncope has been pointed out by Sir Thomas Lewis,[17] but it has not received the attention which it merits.

Attention may be called to the fact that the subject of the above experiment had essential hypertension.* Normal and hypertensive subjects behave very much alike, though individuals in both groups show such differences in sensitivity to diminished venous return that it is difficult to quantitate the renal response. It is enough for the moment to be able to assert that when either the normal or the hypertensive subject assumes the upright, immobile position the blood flow through the kidneys may be substantially reduced by reflex vasoconstriction.

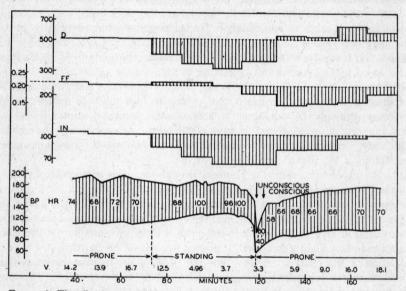

FIGURE 6. The effective renal plasma flow, etc., during syncope induced by the sustained upright posture in a hypertensive subject. Legend as in Figure 1. Note the slowing of the heart rate (HR) which accompanies the fall in blood pressure.

Another circumstance in which neurogenic vasoconstriction can be demonstrated in the kidney is fright[13] (Figure 7). During clearance determinations, this subject suddenly became alarmed through misunderstanding concerning the significance of the clearance procedure. He became increasingly restless, apprehensive, and remonstrative, and sweating and pallor indicated marked autonomic excitation. He was so perturbed that it was impossible to obtain blood pressures, but one feels confident that the mean blood pressure did not fall. When, after 40 minutes, his alarm was abruptly dispelled his apprehension was replaced by relaxation, laughter and the best of humor. The renal vasoconstriction which occurred at the peak of his alarm was as profound as any which we have seen after the administration of large doses of adrenalin, and indeed

* For a discussion of renal function in subjects with essential hypertension see[5, 7, 8]

the vasoconstriction was still present in the last observation. The response is typical of adrenalin and we cannot, of course, exclude the humoral section of this hormone, but in view of the well established relationship between adrenal secretion and sympathetic excitation, it would certainly be arbitrary to exclude the participation of the vasoconstrictor nerves which are abundantly supplied to the kidneys *via* the thoracico-lumbar autonomic outflow, and particularly T10, T11 and T12.

Lastly, it has recently been demonstrated that during the period of hypotension, and indeed sometimes for a period after the blood pressure has been restored to normal by blood transfusion, renal vasoconstriction of marked degree

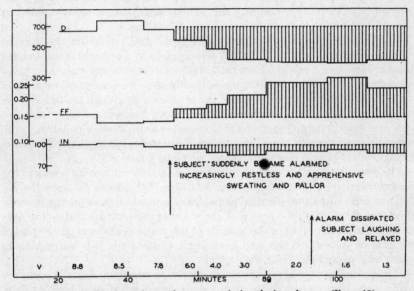

FIGURE 7. Psychogenic renal vasoconstriction during alarm. (From 13)

is present in man when suffering from that form of circulatory failure known as traumatic 'shock'.[10] The degree of vasoconstriction roughly parallels the severity of circulatory inadequacy. Since the available data indicate that circulatory failure issues from decreased venous pressure and leads, even in the face of increased peripheral resistance, to decreased blood pressure, it may be supposed that at least under extreme conditions the renal circulation is subservient to the welfare of the organism as a whole.

Summarizing the more important facts available today, the picture which we have of the normal human kidney is an organ composed of a million-odd nephric units, each presumably capable of functioning more or less independently of the other, in which the blood flow, both glomerular and tubular, is determined by the autonomous activity of the glomerular apparatus or other local vascular devices; connection with the autonomic nervous system is unnecessary for the maintenance of local renal vasomotor tone, and the autonomic nervous system contributes little if anything to the regulation of renal blood flow under basal, resting conditions. The two kidneys normally receive about one-quarter of the total cardiac output. In spite of the fact that the basal renal blood flow is only about half of the apparent maximal value, it appears that all the glomeruli and tubules are active in the basal condition, in that all the available nephrons are active in glomerular filtration and tubular excretion. However, the renal blood flow can be substantially decreased by adrenalin and sympathetic excitation, and increased by the pyrexial reaction, the maximal flow being perhaps 100 percent above the basal value. The actions of adrenalin and pyrogen are both mediated primarily by changes in the efferent glomerular arterioles, which circumstance, in view of the nature of the glomerular circulation, tends to maintain a constant filtration rate, regardless of renal blood flow.

Pyrexial hyperemia is attributable either to the direct action of the pyrogen or some associated constituent on the arterioles, or to a humoral agent secreted into the blood as a result of foreign protein stimulation. In any case, the hyperemia occurs in the denervated kidney as readily as in the innervated organ. In view of the relatively large fraction of the cardiac output which the two kidneys in man normally receive, variations in renal blood flow assume importance not only in respect to the kidneys but also in respect to the systemic circulation. The recent demonstration of renal vasoconstriction in traumatic shock implies a safeguard of considerable magnitude aginst circulatory failure.

The demonstration of renal vasoconstriction in traumatic shock points to the danger inherent in conducting experiments upon the kidneys (as upon the circulation generally) in anesthetized and operated animals. Occasion was recently presented in reviewing the history of the study of the renal circulation[13] to note an unfortunate disregard of the hazards of traumatic procedures on the part of students of kidney function, and in closing this discussion it is warrantable to quote two paragraphs from that review:

'The technique of study of the renal circulation which has been in vogue for many years consists of a series of operations which might have been specially designed to excite autonomic nervous activity. First an anesthetic is administered, then the abdomen is incised and the viscera are exposed and pushed aside; blood vessels are dissected free and ligated, and sometimes the aorta and all its lower branches, other than the renal artery, are tied. The kidney is then forcibly freed of its attachments and manipulated in order to insert a stromuhr in the renal artery or vein, or the entire organ is thrust into an oncometer and put under some pressure. Every surgeon recognizes that laparotomy complicated by even slight visceral trauma presents a circulatory hazard, and circulatory inadequacy due to decreased venous pressure and reduced cardiac filling is imminent in all anesthetized experimental animals wherein the flaccid skeletal muscles and the open abdomen encourage the stagnation of blood. Moreover, such animals are usually either over-heated or over-cooled and suffer progressive hemoconcentration and oligemia. There is little a priori doubt that venous pressure and cardiac filling are embarrassed in a dog or cat whose legs are forcibly extended while it is tied upon its back. If under these conditions vasoconstrictor activity does not approach a maximal level, it must indeed be because of the reign of chaos in the autonomic nervous system, or because the hardy and almost indomitable receptor systems of the aortic arch, the carotid sinus and other vasosensitive zones are either fatigued or depressed below the level of response. When we add to this confusion the possibility that the anesthetic, which may be concentrated in the tubular urine, may just as well disturb the responses of the renal circulation as those of the cerebral cortex, it may safely be inferred that the anesthetized animal is no easy place for the physiologist to find his way about. Surgeons have long been aware of the autonomic disturbances associated with all forms of anesthesia; physiologists, less concerned with the ultimate fate of their experimental subjects, have as long remained stubbornly oblivious to them.'

And in regard to the demonstration of psychogenic vasoconstriction during alarm:

'We do not suppose that every alarm and apprehension has its concomitant of increased renal vasoconstrictor tone: the autonomic nervous system is too complex for easy generalization. I present these observations chiefly that I may return to an earlier point: If emotional disturbance, even of an extreme nature, can so markedly influence the renal circulation in man, what must we say of procedures in laboratory animals which entail profound and almost maximal sympathetic excitation by alarm and fright, by the administration of anesthetic, by excitation of sensory nerves, by surgical incisions, by the handling of the viscera, by circulatory inadequacy, by the manipulation of the kidney itself? I would enter no special plea for the uncontrolled use of the clearance method in renal physiology until it has been more rigorously tested, and other methods are greatly needed to reinforce and supplement it. What I would plead is that the history of renal physiology has been in too large measure a history of traumatic procedures which have in the end only misled investigation; and that far more is to be gained by spending several years in perfecting a non-traumatic, truly physiological method than one year in applying a traumatic one. Perhaps it is not too much to suggest that, so far as immediate experimental procedures are concerned, any observation that is too traumatic to be safely, reasonably and ethically carried out upon man is too traumatic, as far as physiological validity is concerned, to be carried out upon an experimental animal.'

REFERENCES

1. BRADLEY, S. E., AND BING, R. J., Renal function in the harbor seal (*Phoca vitulina* L.) during asphyxial ischemia and pyrogenic hyperemia. J. Cell. and Comp. Physiol., 19: 2, April 1942.
2. BRADLEY, S. E., CHASIS, H., RANGES, H. A., AND GOLDRING, W., Hemodynamic changes during pyrogenic reaction in normal and hypertensive subjects. In preparation.
3. BRADLEY, S. E., AND RANGES, H. A., Systemic and renal circulatory changes following the administration of adrenin, ephedrine, and paredrinol to normal man. J. Clin. Invest. In press.
4. CHASIS, H., RANGES, H. A., GOLDRING, W., AND SMITH, H. W., The control of renal blood flow and glomerular filtration in normal man. J. Clin. Invest., 17: 683, 1938.

5. CHASIS, H., AND REDISH, J., Effective renal blood flow in the separate kidneys of subjects with essential hypertension. J. Clin. Invest., 20: 655, 1941.
6. GADDUM, J. H., The alkaloid ephedrine. Brit. Med. J., 1: 713, 1938.
7. GOLDRING, W., AND CHASIS, H., Hypertension and hypertensive disease. In
   preparation.
8. GOLDRING, W., CHASIS, H., RANGES, H. A., AND SMITH, H. W., Effective renal blood
   flow in subjects with essential hypertension. J. Clin. Invest., 20: 631, 1941.
9. HIATT, E. P., The effect of denervation on the filtration rate and blood flow in dog
   kidneys rendered hyperemic by administration of pyrogen. Amer. J. Physiol.,
   136: 38–41, 1942.
10. LAUSON, H. D., BRADLEY, S. E., AND COURNAND, A., Renal circulation in shock. In
    preparation.
11. LEWIS, T., Vasovagal syncope and the carotid sinus mechanism. Brit. Med. J., 1:
    873, 1932.
12. MEYER, F., AND SPIEGELHOFF, W., Der Einfluss peripher angreifender Kreislaufmittel
    auf Hersleistung, arteriellen Windkessel und Strömungswiderstand. Arch. f.
    Exp. Path. u. Pharm., 190: 256, 1938.
13. SMITH, H. W., The physiology of the renal circulation. Harvey Lectures, 35: 166–222,
    1939–40.
14. SMITH, H. W., Is essential hypertension of renal origin. Bull. N. Y. Acad. Med.
15. SMITH, H. W., CHASIS, H., AND RANGES, H. A., Suitability of inulin for intravenous
    administration to man. Proc. Soc. Exper. Biol. and Med., 37: 726, 1938.
16. SMITH, H. W., GOLDRING, W., CHASIS, H., RANGES, H. A., AND BRADLEY, S. E., Wil-
    liam Henry Welch Lectures. II. The Application of Saturation Methods to
    the Study of Glomerular and Tubular Function in the Human Kidney. J.
    Mount Sinai Hosp., 10: 59, 1943.
17. SMITH, H. W., ROVENSTINE, E. A., GOLDRING, W., CHASIS, H., AND RANGES, H. A.,
    The effects of spinal anesthesia on the circulation in normal, unoperated man
    with reference to the autonomy of the arterioles, and especially those of the
    renal circulation. J. Clin. Invest., 18: 319, 1939.
18. STARR, I., GAMBLE, C. J., MARGOLIES, A., DONAL, JR., J. S., JOSEPH, N., AND EAGLE, E.,
    A clinical study of the action of 10 commonly used drugs on cardiac output,
    work and size; on respiration, on metabolic rate and on the electrocardiogram.
    J. Clin. Invest., 16: 700, 1937.
19. WEZLER, K., AND BÖGER, A., Der arterielle Gesamtwiderstand unter verschiedenartigen
    Sympathicusreizen. Arch. f. exper. Path. u. Pharmakol., 187: 65, 1937.

RENAL PHYSIOLOGY
BETWEEN TWO WARS

RENAL PHYSIOLOGY BETWEEN TWO WARS

It was in the summer of 1920, while recovering from an appendectomy, that A. N. Richards conceived the idea of so arranging a frog's kidney that he could examine the glomeruli directly under a microscope. It may seem that there is no great amount of inventive ingenuity in this procedure, yet it constitutes a milestone in the history of renal physiology. And behind it was what one might call a flowing tide of ideological necessity: a tide on which Richards and his coworker Schmidt were but flotsam and jetsam, destined to be cast up on the shores of science in a new experiment. The waves of ideological necessity which bear men to their experimental fates are frequently as interesting as the experiments which they produce, and are worthy, in this case at least, of a close examination.

Richards, while giving a course in experimental pharmacology at the College of Physicians and Surgeons between 1903 and 1908, had become interested in the isolated mammalian heart as a means of studying the action of drugs upon this organ. With John Howland, he had also been struggling with liver function, particularly those problems concerning detoxification, and it had seemed to him that an adequate perfusion technique, one better than any hitherto described, might unlock the answers to many circulatory and hepatic problems. He had formulated a plan for an ideal perfusion pump not involving any metal, when he moved to Pennsylvania as Professor of Pharmacology in 1910. In the summer of 1911, Cecil K. Drinker came to work with him and they constructed a machine which successfully perfused the brain of a cat for nearly two hours. Just as they were beginning to perfuse a kidney with some success, as measured by an encouraging trickle of urine, Drinker had to leave Philadelphia to start his internship at the Peter Bent Brigham Hospital.

Oscar H. Plant took Drinker's place and during the next year or so he and Richards completed a series of experiments in which they showed that urine formation was related primarily to the blood pressure in, rather than the blood flow through, the kidney, thus offering a rebuttal to an argument that stemmed from Heidenhain, who had found that the rate of excretion of certain dyes is roughly proportional to the blood flow[1], and generally independent of the blood pressure. More noteworthy, however, was their observation that adrenalin in proper doses caused the kidney to swell, even though at the same time it caused a rise in the perfusion pressure required to maintain a constant blood flow.

[1] The relative importance of blood flow and blood pressure in determining the function of the kidneys had been a matter of controversy for nearly fifty years. The modern demonstration that the excretion of many dyes and other substances (phenol red, diodrast, various hippuric acid derivatives, etc.) *is* proportional to blood flow and *not* to the rate of water excretion (which is what the earlier workers generally meant by "urine formation") reveals that there was some basis of truth for Heidenhain's contention.

This paradox was difficult to explain in conventional terms of vasomotor action, which required vasodilatation, and therefore a decrease in perfusion pressure, as the basis for the expansion of an organ; but Richards and Plant soon resolved the difficulty by suggesting that the locus of action of the adrenalin was the *efferent* glomerular arterioles, constriction of which would cause swelling of the glomeruli and anterior portions of the vascular bed at the same time that it caused an increase in perfusion resistance, and therefore in overall perfusion pressure.

Then in April of 1917 came the war, and these experiments, except for a preliminary note, went unpublished for five years. In August of 1917 Richards went to England as consultant to the British Medical Research Committee. In 1917–18 his investigations were confined to some experiments with Dale on the paradoxical action of histamine on isolated organs, in contrast to organs *in situ*, experiments planned in an effort to gain some light on the genesis of traumatic shock. In the interval before he went across the Channel to take charge of the Physiological Laboratory of the Chemical Warfare Service at Chaumont in 1918, he also met Arthur Cushny, and the two became close friends.

Cushny had obtained his M.D. degree at Aberdeen in 1892, and had come as Professor of Pharmacology to the University of Michigan at the age of twenty-seven. In 1905 he had returned to the Chair of Materia Medica and Pharmacology at the University of London, and in 1918 had gone as Professor of Pharmacology to Edinburgh, a Chair which he held until his death in 1926.

His monograph on "The Secretion of Urine," which appeared in 1917, has been described as the first coherent theory of the mode of action of the kidney which accorded with modern knowledge of physical chemistry, even as his textbook on "Pharmacology and Therapeutics and the Action of Drugs" was the first comprehensive textbook on this subject. Dixon, writing of Cushny at the time of his death in 1926 remarked, "The present generation has little understanding of the sacrifices which men like Cushny made to pursue their ideal. Nowadays, men fitted for research can obtain an ample wage, but in those days (1900–1926) £100 per annum was affluence; and it is small wonder that the few like Cushny, who for a time survived, leave a mark on history which is ineradicable."

When Cushny came into the field, the physiology of the kidney was made up, as he said, of "a wrangle of two great views of its activity." In a wrangle, the man who can talk the most usually comes out on top, even though his position may be insecure. It was Cushny's wish to reduce the loose talk and confounded theories then enveloping the kidney to a minimum, while expanding in some small measure the body of solid fact. With a determination that amounted almost to cruelty to theorists, he relegated their confused papers, which he said were more marked for their length than depth, to the library where they could be allowed to continue to collect dust as was their proper fate, while he sought out and organized a few tangible facts which he thought everyone could and would believe.

Cushny came into renal physiology by way of the intestinal tract. Back in 1897–98 at Ann Arbor he and George Wallace had been studying the action of saline cathartics; they had found that sulfates and phosphates are not easily absorbed through the intestinal epithelium and had ascribed the catharsis induced by these salts to the osmotic pressure thereby set up in the intestinal contents. It was but a short step to argue that sulfate and phosphate diuresis is similarly the result of the failure of these salts to be reabsorbed by the renal tubule. A simple notion, but against the background of the last decade of the nineteenth century, a profound one. When Hans Meyer spoke of sulfate diuresis as "renal catharsis," he summed up the new idea in catch phrase.

In subsequent years Cushny came under the influence of Starling, and indeed Starling was the editor of the series of "Monographs on Physiology" of which Cushny's work ("The Secretion of Urine") was the second volume. It is interesting to note in passing that the first of this series had been Gaskell's "Involuntary Nervous System," while the later members included Sherrington's "Physiology of Reflex Action," Keith Lucas' "Conduction of the Nervous Impulse," Dale's "The Physiological Basis of the Action of Drugs," Fletcher's "Nature of Muscular Movement," Mott's "The Cerebral Mechanisms of Speech," and Lovett Evans' "Tissue Respiration." A more distinguished coterie of monographs has certainly never been published.

But to return to the editor, Starling, or rather to the author of the second of Starling's series, Cushny, it was certainly the one who influenced the other towards the acceptance of a belief in a simple physical process of glomerular filtration which owes its origin to the hydrostatic pressure of the blood, and owes nothing to the vital nature of the glomerular capillaries except some degree of impermeability to the plasma proteins.

In 1917 Colonel Starling was in Egypt fighting World War I, and it was there that he read the manuscript of Cushny's monograph. That monograph seems cumbersome now, because from the beginning the author has to fight his way through a maze of elective theories—apart from laboratory data of the first order there were no facts, not even the central idea of glomerular filtration could be set forth as a demonstrated fact. Consequently Cushny endeavored to prepare the way for the student, lest he become wholly lost in the vapors of contradictory speculation, by setting forth what he aptly called his "Modern Theory."

Accepting the premise that urine formation begins in the glomerulus with ultrafiltration, at the expense of the hydrostatic pressure of the blood, of a filtrate containing all the plasma constituents other than the molecularly gigantic proteins, Cushny sought to preserve simplicity by positing that it was the sole function of the renal tubules to reabsorb from this filtrate a fluid of constant and optimal composition, a perfected Locke's solution or protein-free plasma, in such optimal quantities as are required to maintain the optimal composition of the plasma. What was left behind in the tubules passes on into the bladder as urine. "The formation of the glomerular filtrate," he said, "is due to a blind physical force, the absorption in the tubules is equally independent of any discrimination, for the fluid absorbed is always the same, whatever the needs of the organism at the moment."

In retrospect, we can question if the reabsorption of a fluid of "optimal composition" and containing several dozen substances, the conservation of which is advantageous to the organism, is indeed a simplification over the alternative hypothesis that the renal tubules reabsorb these substances independently, in accordance with as yet unidentified factors determining the reabsorption of each substance more or less separately.[2] The past twenty years have shown that the latter explanation is actually the case: tubular reabsorption of each constituent does in fact proceed more or less independently of the reabsorption of other constituents; so perhaps our philosophical quibble about "simplicity" is only hindsight. Nevertheless, one thinks that Cushny would have been happy to have had each valuable constituent of the glomerular filtrate reabsorbed independently were it not that this explanation seemed to entail a terrifying multiplicity of operations on the part of the tubule cells, and this multiplicity of function was just what Cushny was determined to expel from renal physiology. And for a very good reason: multiplicity of function is apt to become elastic, even elective, until running riot it escapes from all descriptive rules and becomes a rule into itself. It ends in vitalism, wherein every cell operates in mysterious ways and under its own wilful determination to achieve some far-off, if not divine, event. Vitalism was still a living issue in Cushny's day, it had scarcely been expelled from nerve-muscle physiology,[3] while many explanations of renal activity were essentially vitalistic in nature. Cushny had no desire to aid and abet this enemy of deterministic science. As he says of his monograph, "If it serves as an advance post from which others may issue against the remaining ramparts of vitalism its purpose will be attained."

But such are the difficulties inherent in ideas, and in the words which we use to designate them, that on page 53 of this same monograph Cushny says that the reabsorption by the tubules of an optimal quantity of fluid of an optimal composition "depends on the *vital* activity of the epithelium." Reducing vital activity to these two by four dimensions and depriving it of the prerogatives of qualitative and quantitative discrimination seems to be a matter of confining the vital force by dialectic chains.

It was, however, not the multiplicity of tubular reabsorptive processes that

[2] Water, Na, K, Ca, PO_4, Cl, HCO_3, glucose, various amino-acids, vitamins, hormones . . . not all these substances have been studied in detail but the available information is sufficient to indicate that the list is a large one. For recent studies on the reabsorption of water, Na and Cl see Shannon (26 27), of K see Winkler and Smith (37), of PO_4 see Harrison and Harrison (11), of SO_4 see Goudsmit and Keith (10), of glucose see Shannon, Farber and Troast (28), of amino-acids see Doty (7), of vitamin C see Friedman, Sherry and Ralli (8), of hemoglobin see Monke and Yuile (19).

[3] Sherrington's monograph on the "Integration of the Nervous System" had not yet been written.

worried Cushny, but the presumed process of tubular secretion, in which the tubular cells were supposed to abstract from the blood, this, that and the other constituent and deposit them in the tubular urine. If we posit the tubular secretion of three diverse substances we seem to require a three-fold discrimination on the part of the tubule cells, and why stop at three? Why not say ten, fifty or a hundred diverse substances are excreted by the tubules, which know just what to pick up out of the blood, just when to abstract it, and just how much to excrete?

Heidenhain had posited the existence of a process of secretion not only in the tubules but in the glomeruli themselves, which he supposed secreted water and salts, and from his time on whenever an investigator found himself in difficulty with an experimental fact he had too frequently been prone to invoke tubular secretion to explain it. It is a case of simple arithmetic: if you have three explanations, glomerular filtration, tubular reabsorption, and tubular secretion, you can dispose of the most horrendous unknown by the judicious application of two out of the three available solutions. In the first quarter of the century renal physiology was the sporting ground for this kind of dialectic, and it was Cushny's determination to drive the deterministically offensive one, tubular secretion, out of the field. His position was that when the adherents of tubular secretion came across with some believable and convincing evidence they would be admitted to respectability; until then they were *persona non grata*.

It was in this milieu of the Cushny renal renaissance that Richards came home from the War in December 1918. Getting together with Plant, they wrote up their experiments on the perfused kidney, guided by Cushny's analysis of the evidence on renal theory. Then in the Spring of 1920 Richards was invited to give a Harvey Lecture and immediately thereafter he came down with an acute appendix. In the ensuing forced vacation he pored over his perfusion experiments and the adrenalin paradox, some reprints of Krogh's papers on capillaries, and Cushny's monograph. Filled with admiration for Krogh's technique of direct observation of the capillaries in the tongue, foot and mesentery of the frog, he conceived that if he could see the glomeruli at work he might obtain a confirmation of the Richards-Plant adrenalin paradox, and thus in his Harvey Lecture be able to present a demonstrated fact rather than an hypothesis. When he got back to the laboratory in the early Autumn he suggested the experiment to Carl F. Schmidt, then an instructor in his department.

No sooner said than done, and what Richards and Schmidt saw under the microscope is now familiar to every student of renal physiology. On the ventral surface of the kidney an occasional glomerulus could be discerned, the capsule distended with fluid, the blood cells moving in a thick stream through the active capillary loops. The most cursory examination showed that the circulation in some glomeruli was much more active than the circulation in others; and indeed in any one glomerulus the number of active capillaries showed considerable variability, a single capillary passing in the course of a short time from a state of activity, wherein the blood flow was abundant, to one of inactivity in which the motion of the cells was slow or wholly arrested. Thus Richards and Schmidt came to speak of the "intermittency of glomerular activity," and to conclude that in the normal kidney not all glomeruli are active at any one time.

These observations on the intermittency of glomerular activity in the frog have been repeatedly confirmed, but their implications for the mammalian kidney are not yet clear after a period of twenty years, and we may set the question of intermittency aside for a moment while considering other features of the experiment. It was all pretty exciting stuff. I can remember hearing about it in Boston, where I had just come to Walter Cannon's department as a National Research Council Fellow. In fact, I heard so much about it in Boston that for a considerable period I labored under the impression that the experiment had been done at Harvard. The basis for this confusion was probably the circumstance that Joseph Wearn, who had been an assistant resident at the Brigham Hospital in 1919 to 1921, went to Philadelphia in the summer of 1921 to join Richards as instructor in pharmacology. Wearn probably sent back such glowing reports on the frog kidney, and they were received with such interest, that out on Longwood Avenue the invention seemed to be indigenous.

It was Wearn who now undertook with Richards the application of the Chambers' microdissection technique to the examination of the composition of the glomerular fluid, Schmidt having left Philadelphia for China. The microdissection technique was not all planned out in advance, like a well-fought military campaign. Richards simply showed Wearn how to look at a frog kidney, asked him to perfect himself in the technique, and to go on looking at it; but to come to him if he had any ideas. Meanwhile, Richards was drifting around and drifted into a meeting of anatomists in which Robert Chambers was demonstrating his microdissecting needle. It occurred to Richards, and he talked it over with Wearn one night after dinner, that Chambers' technique might enable them to test their explanation of the adrenalin paradox by applying the drug directly to the afferent and efferent arteriole. Wearn went farther, and suggested that they puncture the glomerular capsule, withdraw the capsular fluid and analyze it. Fired with enthusiasm, they tackled this difficult task and finally succeeded.

The full development of the micro-study of the kidney was a long and arduous affair. Fifteen years elapsed before the definitive publications on the composition of glomerular and tubular urine made their appearance from the Philadelphia laboratories. Arthur Walker joined the staff in 1925, and in later years James Bordley, John Barnwell, R. C. Bradley, Phyllis Bott, and B. B. Westfall. The painstaking elaboration of capillary analytical methods applicable to the minute amounts of fluid collected from a glomerular capsule or a renal tubule is in itself an achievement of no small importance. The first paper by Wearn and Richards recorded that the glomerular fluid is essentially free of protein, but contains sugar even when simultaneous bladder urine is sugar-free. Cushny was delighted with that result. Subsequent papers developed the quantitative technique until it could be said that in the capsule fluid, or glomerular urine, the glucose, phosphate, urea, uric acid, phenol red and creatinine concentration is just what would be expected in a protein-free ultrafiltrate.[4] Thus the doctrine of glomerular filtration now rests upon a bed of fact.[5]

The study of tubular function had necessarily to be carried out in a more or less random fashion, puncturing a tubule wherever it presented itself in a vulnerable position and blocking it fore or aft with a droplet of mercury; but by this method it was shown that glucose and phosphate are reabsorbed in the proximal tubule, and chloride in the distal tubule; that it is in the distal tubule that the urine is acidified, and in the distal tubule that the urine is made hypotonic to the blood.

Thus there was substantiated the filtration-reabsorption theory, in its broader terms, as it had been formulated in the most elementary sense by Ludwig in 1844, and accepted with slight modification by Cushny in his "Modern Theory" in 1917.

But there remained the vexing question of tubular secretion: did it actually exist, and if so, what part did it play in the formation of urine?

It might seem that the micro-study technique would quickly answer this question, but the answer was not so easy to attain. Recognizing that highly varying quantities of water are reabsorbed from the glomerular filtrate as it passes down the tubules, one cannot say from the degree to which any particular constituent is concentrated over and above the original glomerular filtrate (or, if you wish, the plasma) whether that degree of concentration is due to tubular secretion or merely to the reabsorption of water. Indeed, even if tubular secretion is dismissed *a priori*, one cannot say whether various urinary constituents have been in part reabsorbed. What is required in order to answer the question is a *standard of reference for water reabsorption*, some substance which can be demonstrated to be neither reabsorbed nor secreted by the tubules; then from the degree of concentration of this standard of reference one can

[4] A summary of this work is given by Richards in his Croonian Lecture (23), in his second Harvey Lecture (21) of which he justly made Arthur Walker co-author, and in the Carpenter Lecture (22). Detailed papers appear in the American Journal of Physiology, 118: 111–173, 193″.

Walker, Bott, Oliver and MacDowell (36) have recently extended the micro-technique to rats and guinea pigs and shown that glomerular fluid, entirely or nearly free of protein, contains reducing substances and creatinine in concentrations similar to those existing in plasma rates. All the reducing substances (glucose) and at least two-thirds of the fluid are reabsorbed in the proximal tubule, where some chloride reabsorption also occurs, the proximal tubular urine remaining isotonic with plasma.

Bott and Richards (5) have shown that the glomerular membranes are coarse enough to permit the passage of particles of 20 A. in diameter, with some passage of particles of 50 A. (mol. wgt. of roughly 58,000).

[5] Including the recent work on the rat and guinea pig, the demonstration of glomerular filtration in cold blooded animals may be considered an inadequate basis for accepting the simple, physical nature of the process in all animals. An almost equally cogent demonstration that the principle applies to dog and man is, however, available in the study of simultaneous clearances, described later in this paper.

determine the extent of reabsorption of water, and hence whether any other substance has been reabsorbed or secreted. But before that standard of reference was to come, the question of tubular secretion was destined to be answered in the affirmative by E. K. Marshall, Jr.

Trained as a chemist before he went into medicine at Hopkins, Marshall's development of the urease method in 1912 had led him, in collaboration with D. M. Davis, to make observations on the distribution of urea throughout various organs in the body. One day Marshall and Davis happened upon two dogs which had been adrenalectomized by Samuel Crowe, and discovered the marked retention of urea which follows adrenalectomy.[6] This led them into a study of the influence of the adrenals on the kidneys and, prior to the War, in collaboration with A. C. Kolls, Marshall had started a series of experiments designed to study the influence of the nerves on renal function, experiments which were set aside when he took up work on war gases in New Haven in the summer of 1917. Here, however, he read Cushny's monograph and came to feel that some of the results which he and Kolls had obtained were incompatible with a simple filtration-reabsorption theory.

In the Fall of 1917 Marshall went to the Chemical Warfare Station at American University in Washington, D. C., and it was here that I met him the first week in January of 1918. I had originally been assigned to a battalion of Liquid Flame Throwers in the Engineers, but through the good graces of Col. Wilder D. Bancroft I was transferred to American University where I worked with Marshall and Lynch on mustard gas.

The war over, and gas warfare no longer of interest, Marshall returned to Hopkins where with Kolls he published their pre-war experiments, with additions, in 1919. By this time Marshall had become intrigued with the ambiguities and mysteries of tubular function, and in 1923 he and J. L. Vickers published a paper entitled "The Mechanism of the Elimination of Phenolsulphonephthalein by the Kidney, a Proof of Secretion by the Convoluted Tubules." This proof consisted of the demonstration that after intravenous injection of phenolsulphonephthalein the dye accumulates in the cortex of the non-secreting kidney at a time when the blood pressure is too low to permit the formation of significant quantities of filtrate; and, second, that the dye is to a great extent absorbed or combined with plasma protein, only a small fraction being filtrable; consequently, the quantity of free and filtrable dye in the plasma is inadequate on any acceptable estimation of the rate of filtration to account for the total quantity excreted in a given time. In retrospect, the arguments in this paper are unassailable and must, I think, be taken as the first demonstration of tubular secretion in the mammalian kidney.[7]

These experiments were followed in the next year by a paper by Marshall and Crane, adding new and equally convincing evidence, in the demonstration

---

[6] This retention is now known to be a consequence of circulatory-renal failure.

[7] See 16 and 14. If the evidence of this paper was unconvincing to many, no doubt of tubular excretion could remain after Marshall's (12) demonstration in 1931 that 70 per cent of the phenol red in the renal arterial blood is removed in one passage through the kidney, despite the fact that only 25 per cent is filtrable.

that as the plasma level of phenol red is raised the rate of excretion ultimately levels off and approaches a constant, maximal value; this result is incompatible with a theory of exclusive filtration, but is explicable in terms of filtration plus tubular secretion, the secretory cells becoming saturated at higher plasma levels. At this same time Mayers adduced equally good evidence for the secretion of uric acid by the chicken kidney: the quantity excreted at a given plasma level being inconceivably greater than could be excreted by filtration alone, under any plausible assumption concerning renal blood flow and filtration rate.

Here, in effect, the matter stayed for several years. Proponents of the Cushny theory remained skeptical of Marshall's phenol red experiments, while the proponents of tubular secretion became skeptical of their opponents' reason. Then in 1926, Marshall, browsing through comparative anatomy, discovered that a number of fishes had been described which possessed purely tubular kidneys. This fact, of course, immediately evoked Marshall's interest in fish urine. Unfortunately, aglomerular fishes were rather rare,[8] but we happened to have one species, the goosefish, at Salisbury Cove where I had been working in the summer, and Marshall joined us there in the summer of 1926 to study goosefish urine.

Work on the aglomerular fishes had been undertaken independently by J. G. Edwards in the Naples' laboratory, and within a short time it was clear that this purely tubular kidney, which does not even possess a significant arterial blood supply but is perfused entirely by venous blood from the renal portal vein and at a pressure which is probably below the osmotic pressure of the plasma proteins, can excrete all the ordinary urinary constituents: water, creatine, urea, uric acid, magnesium, sulfate, potassium and chloride: and, among foreign substances, iodide, nitrate, thiosulfate, sulfocyanide, indigo-carmin, neutral red and phenol red. About the only three important things it would not excrete were ferrocyanide, protein and glucose. Marshall recalls this negative discovery as the high point of his experiences in renal physiology, and it was from this point that Jolliffe and I took off in our later attempts to find a carbohydrate which could serve as a standard of reference for water reabsorption in the tubules, a search which led, after a false start with ferrocyanide and xylose, to the use of inulin.

So, by 1930, the question of tubular excretion was answered in the affirmative. But, as Richards said in the discussion when Marshall read a paper at Woods Hole on the aglomerular fish, "At last he has found an animal that fits in with his theory!" To prove tubular excretion in an aglomerular fish or the tubular excretion of phenol red in the dog, was only to prove the *possibility* of tubular excretion in other animals; the demonstration really answered no questions so far as the frog or man was concerned, for conceivably the situation might be

[8] The aglomerular fish kidney represents an evolutionary adaptation to a salt-water habitat where, because of the hypertonicity of the environment, water conservation is imperative. The known list of aglomerular fishes represents six families and at least a dozen genera, and includes the familiar toadfish, midshipman, goosefish, batfish, sea horse, and pipefish, while many others have greatly reduced glomerular function. A discussion of the evolution of the vertebrate kidney is given in the Porter Lectures (31) and a discussion of various aspects of this problem is available in other papers (13, 15 29).

different in every species, and certainly it would differ for different substances. Further progress required that a standard of reference by which water reabsorption in the tubules, or to use the corollary of this statement, the rate of glomerular filtration, could be measured.

The renal physiology which I have reviewed up to this point has been rather more qualitative than quantitative. For the quantitative approach we must transfer to another field of investigation, and cut back again to the early part of the century. Strauss in 1903 and Widal and Javal in 1904, had introduced the determination of blood urea into clinical medicine for diagnostic purposes. But this datum by itself was untrustworthy, since it was contingent not only upon the capacity of the kidney to excrete urea but also upon the protein intake. Gréhant in 1904 had tried to use the urine/blood concentration ratio as an index of functional capacity, but this was worse than the blood urea alone, since the concentration of urea in the urine varied with the urine flow, which was of course not only an uncontrolled, but clinically an uncontrollable variable.

Ambard and Weill in 1912 attempted to relate the rate of urea excretion to the blood urea in a dynamic sense, but it so happens that because of back-diffusion the excretion of urea at varying urine flows is a rather complex affair, and Ambard and Weill ended up with an equation that contained two square root radicles.[9] When used empirically, a square root radicle is a mathematician's device to squeeze a correlation out of data in which a simple correlation is not present, and Ambard and Weill's resort to this device did not serve appreciably to clarify renal physiology.

In 1914 Franklin C. McLean, who had been professor of Pharmacology at Oregon, had been studying the blood sugar[10] in diabetes and was on his way to Breslau to work with Minkowski when the abrupt declaration of war stopped him on the Atlantic Seaboard. He went instead to the Rockefeller Institute as a resident. Mathematically minded, McLean had already been intrigued by Ambard's formula, and now he sought to rearrange it into a more rational urea excretion index.[11] Conceiving that this index should be constant in the

[9] Ambard and Weill's equation was

$$\frac{Ur}{\sqrt{\dfrac{D}{\text{Wgt.}}} \; \sqrt{C}}$$

where Ur = blood urea in gm. per liter
  D = rate of excretion of urea in gm. per 24 hours
  C = Urea concentration on the urine in gm. per liter
  K = constant

[10] McLean had made the first blood sugar determinations in this country, using the Bertrand method wherein the copper reduced by something like 100 cc. of plasma was filtered out and weighed.

[11] McLean's (17) formula was

$$\frac{\text{gm. urea per 24 hours} \; \sqrt{\text{gm. urea per liter urine} \times 8.96}}{\text{weight in kg.} \times (\text{gm. urea per liter of blood})^2} = \text{urea excretion index}$$

McLean's reason for making this change was that mathematically the most important factor determining the value of K in the Ambard and Weill formula is the blood urea, and

diseased as well as the normal kidney, he studied two cases of chronic nephritis over a two months' period, while the patients were kept on a low and a high protein diet. He found that the nephritic kidney responds with increased urea excretion in the face of an elevated blood urea just as does the normal kidney, the mechanism of excretion remaining the same, the only difference between the two being that the nephritic kidney, to use the terms current in the period, shows a greater resistance to the passage of urea. Had McLean 'said that the capacity to excrete urea relative to the blood concentration is reduced in the diseased kidney, the description would have been essentially modernized. McLean abandoned this study when he was called to China to organize the Peking Union Medical School, and left renal physiology behind him with his chief, Donald D. Van Slyke.

At about this same time Thomas Addis and D. R. Drury demonstrated that the rate of urea excretion divided by the urea content of the blood was fairly constant if the urine flow was maintained at high levels by water diuresis.[12] Addis thought that the administered water increased the excretory capacity for urea by a nervous or humoral mechanism; actually the diuresis itself, by reducing the back-diffusion of urea, appears to be the chief factor in explaining the constancy of the Addis index under these conditions. But the administration of water apart, the constancy of the Addis ratio still had no explanation in renal physiology. The situation was not inaccurately summed up when, at about this time, on addressing the Academy of Medicine, he closed his remarks with an emphatic "All we know *for certain* about the kidney, is that it makes urine."

One of the chief results of Addis' observations was to force the quantitative mode of thinking into experimental renal physiology in this country. Paradoxically, Addis has good-naturedly deplored to me the invasion of the quantitative and experimental method into clinical medicine: "'There was a time, not so long ago, when physiology was the handmaid of medicine and you know how disastrous was that bondage. But today there seems to me a danger that medi-

---

since only the square root of the rate of excretion of urea and the fourth root of the concentration of urea in the urine are used, moderate impairment of urea excreting capacity might yield a normal value for K. The use of the factor 8.96 merely served to bring the normal urea excretion index to 100.

[12] Addis and his co-workers (1, 2, 3) found a wide variation in normal subjects when the formula of Ambard and Weill was used, and he substituted the simple formula

$$\frac{\text{Urea in one hour's urine}}{\text{Urea in 100 cc. of blood}} = \text{excretion ratio}$$

What Addis' ratio says is that the excretion of urea per unit time is proportional to the concentration in the blood, and independent of the urine volume. (Neglecting the effects of back-diffusion through the tubules, which are most marked at low urine flows, this is essentially the true relationship.) Since the numerator of Addis' ratio is the urea excreted in one hour's urine, the figure actually represents the urea concentration times the hourly volume and, except for the difference in the time element, the ratio is identical with the maximal urea clearance of Möller, McIntosh and Van Slyke; i.e., the Addis ratio when obtained at high urine flows corresponds to an hourly maximal clearance.

For a detailed study of the effect of urine concentration on the tubular reabsorption of urea in the dog, see Shannon (24), and for a similar study in man, see Chasis and Smith (6)

cine may be sterilized by becoming an appendage of physiology.... Young clinicians, dazzled by new experimental methods, are in danger of becoming poor doctors, and they should remember that they are doctors, first, last and all the time." To this I would reply that if the use of quantitative methods and quantitative thinking ends in making poor doctors, it would indeed be tragic, but such need not be the case. I think that quantitatively-minded doctors can be better doctors than qualitatively-minded ones. And I can also retort that my friend Thomas Addis is in considerable measure responsible for the alleged "sterilization" process, in consequence of his pioneer work in this and other problems in renal physiology.

After McLean left the Rockefeller Institute, Van Slyke, working with Austin and Stillman, and later with Möller and McIntosh, showed that the excretory efficiency of the kidney could be expressed simply as *the volume of blood cleared of urea by one minute's excretion*. They called this volume of blood the *urea clearance*. With moderate or abundant diuresis, they found that the kidneys of a normal man excreted on the average the amount of urea contained in 75 cc. of his blood. If the urea content of the blood was increased by urea feeding, the rate of excretion rose parallel with the blood concentration, so that the same 75 cc. of blood were cleared per minute. If the kidneys were damaged by disease, they cleared less blood of urea per minute: in uremia only 3 or 4 cc. or less. The urea clearance was found to be a sensitive clinical measure of renal function. Visualizing, as in a measuring cylinder, the volume of blood which represents the clearance makes it possible to use a mental photograph in place of a mathematical formula.

The clearance is calculated as (mg. urea excreted per minute)/(mg. urea in 1 cc. of blood). If 15 mg. of urea, e.g., are excreted per minute and the blood urea is 0.2 mg. per cc., the clearance is 15/0.2 = 75 cc. of blood per minute.

Expressed in terms of the analytical observed values, urine urea concentration, U and urine volume flow, V, the urea excretion rate is the product UV. Indicating blood urea concentration as B, the clearance assumes the familiar form ordinarily used in its calculation:

$$\text{Clearance} = \frac{UV}{B}$$

If the urine flow fell below about 2 cc. per minute, Van Slyke and his collaborators found that the clearance began to decrease,[13] and between flows of 2 and 0.5 cc. fell approximately in proportion to the square root of the urine volume. In order to use clearances observed with low urine flows as practical measures of renal function it was necessary to correct the observed clearances by multi-

[13] The point at which UV *apparently* became proportional to B (i.e., 2 cc. per minute in man) Austin, Stillman and Van Slyke (4) called the "augmentation limit". This term unfortunately helped to fix the erroneous concept that UV/B was independent of V at urine flows above 2 cc. per minute. Actually the relationship of UV to B is roughly parabolic, the curve rising rapidly at low urine flows, and gradually flattening and approaching as an asymptote the rate of glomerular filtration at very high urine flows (see 24 and 6).

For Möller, McIntosh and Van Slyke's paper see (18).

plying with the correction $1/\sqrt{V}$, when V was less than 2. Multiplying by this factor gives the volume of blood cleared of urea per minute when the urine flow is 1 cc. per minute. Möller, McIntosh, and Van Slyke called this the "standard clearance," because it applied to a standard urine flow of 1 cc. per minute. It averages 54 cc. of blood in normal men.

$$\text{Standard clearance} = \text{observed clearance} \times \frac{1}{\sqrt{V}} \qquad (a)$$

$$= \frac{UV}{B} \times \frac{1}{\sqrt{V}} \qquad (b)$$

$$= \frac{U\sqrt{V}}{B} \qquad (c)$$

To differentiate the higher clearance obtained with abundant urine flows, Möller, McIntosh, and Van Slyke called it the "maximal clearance," since it is the maximum obtainable by accelerating the urine flow.

If in retrospect the square root sign over the V term in Austin, Stillman and Van Slyke's equation for low urine flows was a compromise with the then inexplicable vagaries of urea excretion, Möller, McIntosh and Van Slyke fully compensated in the direction of rationalism when they borrowed, perhaps from economic bankruptcy, the now familiar term "clearance." Like many good things, this term was born of necessity. In 1926 Van Slyke had been on his way to Baltimore to give an address on kidney function, and on the train his courage failed him when he thought of facing an audience again with a mathematical equation. He had learned what every lecturer must ultimately learn, that only experts can visualize and comprehend the true realities which the unreal symbols of a mathematical equation are intended to represent: the simplest equation has the fearsome power of completely dispelling the comprehension of an audience, at least in the fields of medicine. As Van Slyke sat on the train seeking a solution of how to dispense with mathematics for the benefit of the medical profession, it occurred to him that all that the equation for high urine flows said was that in effect some constant volume of blood was being "cleared" of urea in each minute's time.

In my opinion this word has been more useful to renal physiology than all the equations ever written. In recent years it has broken loose from the excretion of urea and, taking conceptual wings, has become a generalized notion applicable to all aspects of renal excretion. We glibly say that the kidneys *clear* the blood of a large variety of substances: in a particular subject and one minute's time 1.0 cc. of blood may be cleared of water, 10 cc. of sulphate, 20 cc. of potassium, 75 cc. of urea, 130 cc. of inulin, 760 cc. of phenol, 1200 cc. of diodrast, without knowing *a priori* how the kidneys clear the blood of these substances, whether by filtration plus tubular reabsorption, filtration without tubular reabsorption, or filtration plus tubular excretion. Urea is cleared first by separation of some approximately constant quantity of glomerular filtrate, and the reason that the urea clearance decreases with decreasing urine flow is because the more the tubular urine is concentrated the more urea diffuses back into the blood. Glucose is also filtered, but the *glucose clearance* is normally zero because all the glucose in the tubular urine is reabsorbed; but phlorizin completely blocks the tubular reabsorption of glucose, and in the phlorizinized animal the glucose clearance rises to a large and relatively constant value. If no glucose is secreted by the renal tubules, and if tubular reabsorption is completely blocked, then the rate at which glucose is cleared in the phlorizinized animal must be equal to the rate at which the glomerular filtrate is formed. But the glucose clearance in the phlorizinized animal is identical (in simultaneous observations!) with the *mannitol clearance*, the *sorbitol clearance*, the *dulcitol clearance*, the *creatinine clearance*, the *sucrose clearance*, and the *inulin clearance*; except for glucose and creatinine, these clearances are also identical in the normal animal: hence the conclusion that in the normal animal, mannitol, sorbitol, dulcitol, sucrose and inulin are excreted by filtration alone, and without tubular reabsorption or tubular secretion. Phlorizin blocks the reabsorption of glucose and brings the glucose clearance up to the level of the filtration rate. The creatinine clearance in both the normal and phlorizinized dog is identical with the simultaneous inulin clearance, but in normal man (and apes) the former is about 30 per cent higher, indicating that in addition to filtration, some creatinine is cleared from the blood by the tubules, as is the case in many of the lower animals. Phlorizin blocks this tubular excretion and brings the total creatinine clearance down to the level of the filtration rate.

If, as in the case of creatinine, the clearance of any substance, such as phenol red or diodrast, is greater than the simultaneous inulin or mannitol clearance, it can only be because some of that substance is cleared by the tubules, in addition to that which is cleared through the glomeruli.[14] But there must be a limit even to the process of tubular clearance: we cannot clear any substance from a larger volume of blood than actually perfuses the kidneys. The clearance of diodrast in normal man, calculated as whole blood, is approximately 1200 cc. per minute—one fourth of the total cardiac output. Obviously, this must be close to the total renal blood flow: i.e., the extraction of this compound from the renal blood must be very nearly complete and for practical purposes we may take the diodrast clearance as identical with the renal blood flow.

No elaborate equations are involved in this brief summary—only the notions of filtration plus tubular reabsorption, or filtration plus tubular excretion. The only mathematical operation required is simply to multiply $U \times V$ and divide by P.

Paradoxically, Möller, McIntosh and Van Slyke confused the issue by calling $U\sqrt{V}/B$ a "clearance," since in fact it is the product of a mathematical operation wherein UV/B is multiplied by $1/\sqrt{V}$, as shown in equations (a), (b) and (c) above; hence in the strict sense it is not a real clearance but a presumed clearance predicated on the assumption that below 2.0 cc. per minute UV/B will

---

[14] On the premise, of course, that the substance under examination is not synthetized by the kidney, which is certainly true of phenol red, diodrast, p-aminohippuric acid and other substances being studied by renal physiologists.

decrease in proportion to $1/\sqrt{V}$, and calculated to the value of $V = 1.0$. The widespread use of the calculation without general recognition of its derivation has served to confuse many workers. The "standard clearance" remains a physiological enigma so long as the V term is under a square root radicle. One of the hardest things students of physiology have to learn is that the two terms: UV, as they occur in the clearance expression, *must never be divorced*; for by joining them in multiplication they become an integer standing for some *quantity* of a substance excreted per unit time, and you cannot without offence to reason break a *quantity* of anything into two dissimilar parts. Neither can you put a square root sign over half of it.

This, I think was my own first lesson in renal physiology.

William Goldring, who was interested in the etiology of nephritis, had gone to the Rockefeller Institute one day in 1928 to meet Dr. Addis in order to discuss with him the Addis count. He could not find Addis and happened to drift into Van Slyke's laboratory where he was asked to sit down and wait. He and Van Slyke fell to talking about renal function tests, and Van Slyke suggested that Goldring ought to do some urea clearances on patients with erysipelas, of which there were a large number in the Bellevue wards. The results, which have never been published, were very confusing.

During the febrile phase of the disease, the urea clearance might be as much as 200 per cent of the Van Slyke normal standard, and then during the afebrile recovery period they might fall to 30 or 40 per cent of the normal standard. Dr. Goldring could not make any sense out of it, and brought the data to me, knowing that I had been interested in the renal physiology of fishes, turtles and the like. This proved to be poor preparation, and I wrestled with his ever-changing standard clearances and maximal clearances, and got nowhere. Sometimes the patient's standard clearance was greater than his maximal clearance on another occasion, and vice versa. I tried some high-flying mathematics of my own (unable to interpret the physiological significance of the square root radicle in the standard clearance) but to no avail. Perhaps three months elapsed before I fully realized that the maximal clearance might mean something quite simple physiologically, but the standard clearance, because of its square root radicle, was an unphysiological and empirical calculation. The standard clearance apart, I began to think of the maximal clearance simply in terms of filtration rate and tubular reabsorption, as Van Slyke had no doubt thought of it when he first used the term. It was soon evident enough that no physiological interpretation could be forthcoming until there was contained in the experiment some thoroughly reliable, simultaneous measurement of the filtration rate.[15]

[15] Rehberg (20) clearly saw the need of such a standard of reference in 1926; he rather arbitrarily chose creatinine for this purpose, on the grounds that creatinine was concentrated in the urine to a greater extent than any other identified constituent in the urine. Recent work, however, demonstrates that creatinine is in part excreted in man by the tubules. The creatinine clearance has, however, been widely if erroneously accepted by European investigators as identical with the filtration rate.

This led, in 1929, to experiments by Norman Jolliffe, showing that xylose is not excreted by the aglomerular fish, and then to further experiments on the dog and man with Jolliffe and subsequently with James A. Shannon. Our first essay on the measurement of the filtration rate using xylose, sucrose and raffinose proved to be wrong, but we were never wholly content with it, and had sought among other carbohydrates for still larger molecules where there could be no possibility of back diffusion. Sometime in 1933 I hit upon the inulin idea, but a laboratory sample proved to be relatively insoluble and I momentarily discarded it. Fresh inulin was ultimately procured and, in the latter part of the year we got down to work with inulin in a serious manner. We discovered then that we were wrong about xylose as a substance suitable for the measurement of the filtration rate, but we were now more than ever convinced that we were right about inulin.[16]

In October of 1934 Richards came to New York to read a paper on kidney function before the Society of Experimental Biology and Medicine, and we discovered that we were working on the same problems and with the same motives and with the same substance. As far back as 1900 when he had been a student under Philip Hiss, the bacteriologist at Columbia, Richards had suggested inulin to Hiss as a polysacchride which might yield only levulose for fermentation. If I am not mistaken, an inulin medium is still in use which is based on that suggestion. Thirty years later when he was racking his brain for a substance suitable for the measurement of glomerular filtration, inulin had recurred to him.

With the introduction of the inulin clearance the way was open to study tubular reabsorption and tubular excretion in a quantitative manner. In 1935 Shannon, studying phenol red excretion in the dog, showed, in accordance with the surmise of Marshall and Crane, that at high plasma levels the tubules do indeed become "saturated" and excrete the dye at a constant maximal rate. This maximal limitation in tubular excretion has subsequently been demonstrated for diodrast and a number of other substances in both dog and man, and may be considered to be a characteristic feature of tubular activity.[17]

It was also in 1935 that Goldring, Clark and Smith pointed out that the phenol red clearance at low plasma levels (where the tubules are not approaching saturation) afforded a close approximation to the renal blood flow. At this point Herbert Chasis joined our group, and a little later, Hilmert Ranges. In 1937 Goldring, Chasis and myself showed that the clearance of diodrast, the tubular excretion of which had been demonstrated by Elsom, Bott and Shiels in Richards' laboratory, afforded a closer and indeed quite satisfactory measure of the renal blood flow; and further, that the maximal rate of tubular excretion of diodrast (or diodrast Tm) could be used to characterize the total quantity of functional tubular tissue in the kidneys, independently of the blood flow or

[16] A long series of papers dealing with simultaneous clearances in various species (fishes, dog and man) is reviewed in the "Physiology of the Kidney" (30), in the Porter Lectures (31), and by Smith, Finkelstein and Smith (35).

[17] Tubular excretion has been reviewed by Shannon (25).

filtration rate.[18] In 1938 Shannon, Farber and Troast showed that a similar, limiting maximal rate characterized the reabsorption of glucose by the tubules and, in line with diodrast Tm, they called this term glucose Tm.

The application of the methods for the measurement of blood flow and filtration rate together with the saturation methods (diodrast Tm and glucose Tm), opens new avenues of approach to the study of the distribution of blood or glomerular filtrate among the functional units of the kidney. We can then return, in our study of the human kidney, to the problem of glomerular intermittency, and its corollary of possible intermittency in tubular perfusion, raised by Richards and Schmidt twenty years ago. This problem, with conjoint studies of the effects of disease upon glomerular and tubular function, comprises the subject of the following paper.

BIBLIOGRAPHY

1. ADDIS, T., AND DRURY, D. R.: The Rate of Urea Excretion. V. The Effect of Changes in Blood Urea Concentration on the Rate of Urea Excretion. J. Biol. Chem. 55: 105, 1923.

2. ADDIS, T., AND DRURY, D. R.: The Rate of Urea Excretion. VIII. The Effect of Changes in Urine Volume on the Rate of Urea Excretion. J. Biol. Chem. 55: 639, 1923.

3. ADDIS, T., SHEVKY, A. E., AND BEVIER, G.: The Regulation of Renal Activity. II. The Balance Between the Regulation by Adrenalin and by Pituitrin. Am. J. Physiol. 46: 129, 1918.

4. AUSTIN, J. H., STILLMAN, E., AND VAN SLYKE, D. D.: Factors Governing the Excretion Rate of Urea. J. Biol. Chem. 46: 91, 1921.

5. BOTT, P. A., AND RICHARDS, A. N.: The Passage of Protein Molecules Through the Glomerular Membranes. J. Biol. Chem. 141: 291, 1941.

6. CHASIS, H., AND SMITH, H. W.: The Excretion of Urea in Normal Man and in Subjects with Glomerulonephritis. J. Clin. Investigation. 17: 347, 1938.

7. DOTY, J. R.: Reabsorption of Certain Amino Acids and Derivatives by the Kidney Tubules. Proc. Soc. Exper. Biol. & Med. 46: 129, 1941.

8. FRIEDMAN, G. J., SHERRY, S., AND RALLI, E. P.: Mechanism of Excretion of Vitamin C by Human Kidney at Low and Normal Plasma Levels of Ascorbic Acid. J. Clin. Investigation. 19: 685, 1940.

9. GOLDRING, W., CHASIS, H., RANGES, A., AND SMITH, H. W.: Relations of Effective Renal Blood Flow and Glomerular Filtration to Tubular Excretory Mass in Normal Man. J. Clin. Investigation. 19: 739, 1940.

10. GOUDSMIT, A., JR., AND KEITH, N. M.: Relative Significance of Concentration of Inorganic Sulfate in the Serum and of its Renal Clearance. Arch. Int. Med. 66: 816, 1940.

11. HARRISON, H. E., AND HARRISON, H. C.: The Renal Excretion of Inorganic Phosphate in Relation to the Action of Vitamin D and Parathyroid Hormone. J. Clin. Investigation. 20: 47, 1941.

12. MARSHALL, E. D., JR.: The Secretion of Phenol Red by the Mammalian Kidney. Am. J. Physiol. 99: 77, 1931.

13. MARSHALL, E. K., JR.: The Comparative Physiology of the Kidney in Relation to Theories of Renal Secretion. Physiol. Rev. 14: 133, 1934.

14. MARSHALL, E. K., JR., AND CRANE, M. M.: The Secretory Function of the Renal Tubules. Am. J. Physiol. 70: 465, 1924.

[18] For the application of these methods to man see 9, 32, 33, 34.

15. MARSHALL, E. K., JR., AND SMITH, H. W.: The Glomerular Development of the Vertebrate Kidney in Relation to Habitat. Biol. Bulletin. 59: 135, 1930.

16. MARSHALL, E. K., JR., AND VICKERS, J. L.: The Mechanism of the Elimination of Phenolsulphonephthalein by the Kidney—a Proof of Secretion by the Convoluted Tubules. Johns Hopkins Hosp. Bull. 34: 1, 1923.

17. McLEAN, F.: The Numerical Laws Governing the Rate of Excretion of Urea and Chlorides in Man. I. An Index of Urea Excretion and the Normal Excretion of Urea and Chlorides. J. Exper. Med. 22: 212, 1915.

18. MÖLLER, E., McINTOSH, J. F., AND VAN SLYKE, D. D.: Studies in Urea Excretion. II. Relationship Between Urine Volume and the Rate of Urea Excretion by Normal Adults. J. Clin. Investigation. 6: 427, 1928.

19. MONKE, J. V., AND YUILE, C. L.: The Renal Clearance of Hemoglobin in the Dog. J. Exper. Med. 72: 149, 1940.

20. REHBERG P. B.: Studies on Kidney Function. I. The Rate of Filtration and Reabsorption in the Human Kidney. Biochem. J. 20: 447, 1926.

21. RICHARDS, A. N.: Urine Formation in the Amphibian Kidney. The Harvey Lectures, 1934–1935.

22. RICHARDS, A. N.: Physiology of the Kidney. Carpenter Lecture. Bull. New York Acad. Med. 14: 2nd series, 1938.

23. RICHARDS, A. N.: Processes of Urine Formation. Proc. Roy. Soc., London Series B, 126: 398, 1938.

24. SHANNON, J. A.: Glomerular Filtration and Urea Excretion in Relation to Urine Flow in the Dog. Am. J. Physiol. 117: 206, 1936.

25. SHANNON, J. A.: Renal Tubular Excretion. Physiol. Rev. 19: 63, 1939.

26. SHANNON, J. A.: The Control of the Renal Excretion of Water. I. The Effect of Variations in the State of Hydration on Water Excretion in Dogs with Diabetes Insipidus. J. Exper. Med. 76: 371, 1942.

27. SHANNON, J. A.: The Control of the Renal Excretion of Water. II. The Rate of Liberation of the Posterior Pituitary Antidiuretic Hormone in the Dog. J. Exper. Med. 76: 371, 1942.

28. SHANNON, J. A., FARBER, S., AND TROAST, L.: The Measurement of Glucose Tm in the Normal Dog. Am. J. Physiol. 133: 752, 1941.

29. SMITH, H. W.: Water Regulation and its Evolution in the Fishes. Quart. Rev. Biol. 7: 1, 1932.

30. SMITH, H. W.: The Physiology of the Kidney. Oxford Press, 1937.

31. SMITH, H. W.: Physiology of the Kidney. Porter Lectures, 9th series, 1939. Univ. of Kansas Press, Lawrence, Ka. Revised, 1943.

32. SMITH, H. W.: The Physiology of the Renal Circulation. The Harvey Lectures, 35: 116, 1939–1940.

33. SMITH, H. W.: Note on the Interpretations of Clearance Methods in the Diseased Kidney. J. Clin. Investigation. 20: 631, 1941.

34. SMITH, H. W., GOLDRING, W., AND CHASIS, H.: The Measurement of the Tubular Excretory Mass, Effective Blood Flow and Filtration Rate in the Normal Human Kidney. J. Clin. Investigation. 17: 263, 1938.

35. SMITH, W. W., FINKELSTEIN N., AND SMITH, H. W.: Renal Excretion of Hexitols (Sorbitol, Mannitol, and Dulcitol) and Their Derivatives (Sorbitan, Isomannide, and Sorbide) and of Endogenous Creatinine-like Chromogen in Dog and Man. J. Biol. Chem. 135: 231, 1940.

36. WALKER, A. M., BOTT, P. A., OLIVER, J., AND MacDOWELL, M. C.: The Collection and Analysis of Fluid from Single Nephrons of the Mammalian Kidney. Am. J. Physiol. 134: 580, 1941.

37. WINKLER, A. W., AND SMITH, P. K.: Renal Excretion of Potassium Salts. Am. J. Physiol. 138: 94, 1942.

APPLICATION OF SATURATION METHODS TO THE STUDY OF GLOMERULAR AND TUBULAR FUNCTION IN THE HUMAN KIDNEY

THE APPLICATION OF SATURATION METHODS TO THE STUDY OF GLOMERULAR AND TUBULAR FUNCTION IN THE HUMAN KIDNEY*

I. INTRODUCTION

In 1924 Richards and Schmidt (28) noted by the direct microscopic observation of the exposed frog's kidney, that in only some of the glomeruli, or in some of the capillaries in individual glomeruli, was the circulation active at any one moment, an observation which has since been confirmed in other cold-blooded animals. It has further been shown that the glomerular circulation can be increased by water diuresis and various drugs, notably caffeine, and decreased by splanchnic stimulation (2, 4, 12, 27, 44). In the frog (15), the alligator (Shannon, unpublished observations) and the marine teleost fishes (9) the rate of glomerular filtration is more or less proportional to the rate of urine formation; while in the marine seal, an animal entirely dependent upon its metabolic water for urine formation, both glomerular filtration and renal blood flow have been shown to increase markedly after the ingestion of food (5, 22). The interrelation between total filtration rate and diuresis in these species indicates that the glomerular circulation is somehow subordinated to physiological control, while in the frog Forster (16) has shown by the application of the glucose saturation method that glomerular intermittency is probably an all or nothing phenomenon.

The notion of intermittent glomerular activity has been transferred to higher animals on the basis of the distribution of dyes injected into the dog and rabbit kidneys (21, 23), but White (45) has concluded that where all the glomeruli of the dog or rabbit are not injected, the unequal distribution of injection fluid is attributable primarily to differences in patency of the larger, preglomerular vessels, rather than inactivity of individual glomeruli, and that under normal conditions all the glomerular vessels are open.

There exist in the human kidney various non-glomerular vascular channels which might permit the direct perfusion of the tubules: the chief types of such channels are represented by exceptional terminal or lateral arterioles which terminate directly in the capillary net of the *cortex corticus*, capsular arterioles which penetrate the cortical capillary net, arterioles stemming from the afferent arterioles to make direct connection with the capillary plexus, or Isaacs-Ludwig

---

*This lecture represents the definitive publication of a series of studies carried out by William Goldring, Herbert Chasis, Hilmert A. Ranges, Stanley E. Bradley and Homer W. Smith.

The substance of this lecture was presented by one of us (H. W. S.) as the Soma Weiss Memorial Lecture under the auspices of Alpha Omega Alpha at the Harvard Medical School on May 14, 1942. A preliminary report was read before the American Physiological Society (25).

arterioles, and *arteriolae rectae verae* which pass directly from the interlobular arteries into the medulla; in addition, direct anastomoses connect the arterioles and veins which might permit the arterial perfusion of at least some portions of the peritubular capillary bed by a retrograde capillary perfusion.[1] (For literature, see 34.) All the above connections are relatively rare and probably of negligible importance in the normal kidney, but it is conceivable that in chronic renal disease one or more types of such channels might, by hypertrophy, come to play an important sustaining or excretory rôle. Indeed, Oliver and his collaborators (24) have shown that arterioles of the Isaacs-Ludwig type do hypertrophy in chronic diffuse glomerulonephritis, and by their exquisite reconstructions they have demonstrated the survival of aglomerular nephrons which have the appearance of functional integrity.

Since the function of non-glomerular arterioles, in either the normal or abnormal kidney, must be related to the maintenance of the tubular blood supply when the glomerular circulation is reduced, their potential importance would be considerably enhanced could it be demonstrated that a substantial fraction of the glomeruli in the normal kidney are inactive at any one time. Hence the problems of intermittent glomerular activity and direct tubular blood supply are essentially interdependent. In broader terms, one might argue *a priori* that the well developed renal-portal (venous) circulation to the tubules which characterizes the kidney in the fishes, amphibia, reptiles and birds, would, by sustaining tubular perfusion, favor intermittent glomerular activity; whereas the complete absence of such a renal-portal circulation in the mammals would militate against intermittent activity.

From the physiologic point of view, our interest in the question of the relative distribution of glomerular activity among various nephrons in the kidney is enhanced by the circumstance that the reabsorptive tubule, which is individually fixed in size, is also limited by certain maximal capacities or rates of activity, and it is fair presumption that the quantity of filtrate delivered to each tubule is somehow conditioned by this circumstance. The relative distribution of tubular perfusion is a conjoint problem: were the distribution of peritubular blood subject to control independently of the glomerular circulation, the glomerular-tubular balance could scarcely fail to be impaired.

The present study is an examination of these problems, utilizing two saturation phenomena known to characterize tubules, namely the reabsorption of glucose and the excretion of diodrast. The study naturally divides itself into three parts: first, the application of the saturation methods to the determination of glucose Tm and diodrast Tm; second, the magnitude of these terms in relation to each other and to the filtration rate, in both the normal and diseased kidney—essentially a statistical study of the normal and abnormal parameters or ideal

---

[1] Springorum (39), combining the thermostromuhr method of measuring renal blood flow in the anesthetized dog with simultaneous measurements of blood pressure in the brachial artery and the renal vein, was unable to discover any evidence of functional arterio-venous anastomoses during vasomotor excitation of various types.

means; and third, the application of the titration method to the frequency distribution problem, wherein glucose saturation is used to determine the distribution of glomerular filtrate, and diodrast saturation is used to determine the distribution of tubular perfusate, among the nephrons of individual subjects.

II. DESCRIPTION OF THE SATURATION METHODS

1. The reproducibility of glucose Tm and diodrast Tm

Shannon and Fisher (32) and Shannon, Farber and Troast (31) have shown in the dog that as the plasma level of glucose is progressively elevated, a point is ultimately reached where the tubular reabsorption of glucose reaches a constant, maximal rate. Below the minimal level of plasma glucose required to effect tubular saturation, reabsorption from the tubular urine is essentially complete; above this minimal level, such glucose as is filtered through the glomeruli in excess of the maximal rate of reabsorption is excreted in the urine. The maximal rate of reabsorption, as measured for the two kidneys, is in any one animal a reproducible value (31) and is independent of the plasma glucose level between the minimal saturating level (typically about 200 mg. per cent in the dog) and 2000 mg. per cent.

The quantity of glucose filtered per minute constitutes the load of glucose offered to the tubules for reabsorption; for the entire kidneys this load (mg. per min.) is the concentration[2] of glucose in the glomerular filtrate, or P_G (mg. per cc.), multiplied by the rate of filtration, C_{IN} (cc. per min.): i.e., glucose load $= P_G C_{IN}$. The rate of tubular reabsorption of glucose, T_G (mg. per min.), is the difference between this load and the quantity of glucose excreted in the urine per minute, or $U_G V$:

$$(1) \qquad T_G = P_G C_{IN} - U_G V$$

where U_G (mg. per cc.) is the urine glucose concentration and V (cc. per min.) is the urine flow. Roughly speaking, as P_G is increased, T_G remains equal to $P_G C_{IN}$ ($U_G V$ being equal to zero) until the maximal reabsorptive capacity is reached. This maximal rate of tubular reabsorption is designated as glucose Tm, or Tm_G.

Where filtration is arrested completely in a glomerulus, the attached tubule will no longer participate in glucose reabsorption and Tm_G will decrease pro-

[2] The concentration of glucose in the glomerular filtrate is greater than in the plasma in consequence of the abstraction of plasma proteins in the filtration process, the true concentration in the filtrate being P_G/W, where W equals 1—per cent of plasma protein/100. But since the true filtration rate in cc. of water is $C_{IN}W$, the term W cancels out of all our equations relating to Tm_G.

To express all "filtration clearances" in terms of plasma water, in conformity with physiologic fact, would be cumbersome, and, as a matter of convenience, it seems desirable to adhere to the generally accepted convention of expressing them as volumes of plasma, introducing the correction W only when quantitatively necessary. The correction is necessary in the calculation of tubular excretion of a solute bound to plasma proteins, as in equation (2) of this paper.

portionally, the decrease in Tm_G being independent of the filtration rate in the remaining nephrons. Short of complete cessation of filtration, the contribution of any unsaturated nephron to T_G will depend upon the load of glucose being delivered to that nephron, *i.e.*, upon the plasma concentration of glucose and the filtration rate in the attached glomerulus (this circumstance affording the basis for the method developed in Part V of this paper for evaluating the distribution of glomerular activity); but at a concentration of glucose high enough to saturate all nephrons having an average rate of filtration, the gross measurement of T_G may be expected to afford a rough index of the number of active glomeruli.

In an analogous manner, elevation of the plasma concentration of diodrast leads ultimately to the saturation of the excretory mechanism of the tubules, under which conditions they excrete diodrast at a fixed and reproducible rate (37).

The rate of tubular excretion of diodrast, T_D, is given by the difference between the total rate of excretion $U_D V$, and the rate of diodrast filtration, the latter being given by the product of the plasma concentration, P_D, times the rate of glomerular filtration, C_{IN}, times the fraction of free, filterable diodrast in the plasma, FW^3; *i.e.*,

$$(2) \qquad\qquad T_D = U_D V - FW P_D C_{IN}$$

The load of diodrast carried to the tubules must be calculated from the plasma concentration, P_D, and the renal plasma flow, as estimated from the diodrast clearance, C_D. For a discussion of this calculation the reader is referred to equation 14. It is sufficient to remark here that when P_D is high enough to maintain tubular saturation, T_D has a maximal value and is designated as diodrast Tm, or Tm_D.

Complete ischemia of any tubule will result in that tubule dropping out of the process of diodrast excretion, and hence in a proportional decrease in Tm_D, this decrease being independent of the quantity of blood perfusing other tubules.

2. Determination of definitive Tm_G

Table I presents data on six normal subjects showing the reproducibility of Tm_G under standard conditions, either determined on different occasions or at different load/T_G ratios on the same occasion. In addition, repeated determinations were made on eight of the subjects listed in Table II. Of 20 repeated determinations, 16 agree within 5 per cent, the exceptions being E. B. and H. M. (6 per cent), T. S. (8 per cent), and P. M. (12 per cent).

Shannon and his co-workers (31, 32) have shown in the dog that T_G does not increase when the load/T_G ratio is increased from 1.0, or slightly above, to

---

[3] W appears in this equation because the nomogram of Smith and Smith (38) relates the equilibrium concentration of free diodrast per 100 cc. of *plasma water* (ultrafiltrate) to the concentration of total diodrast per 100 cc. of *plasma*; when the concentration in the filtrate is referred back to plasma, as in the term P_D, it is diluted by protein to the extent of W, where $W = 1.00$—per cent protein/100.

10.0. In no case have we endeavored to reach such a high ratio as the latter figure and believe that it would be impractical in most subjects, since under these conditions the urine flow is very large and very rapid infusions must be given to prevent dehydration.[4] We do not in general recommend raising P_G above 700 mg. per cent; in a subject in whom C_{IN} is relatively high (e.g., 140) and Tm_G relatively low (e.g., 300) this will yield a load/T_G ratio of 3.27; but if the above figures are 100 and 400, respectively, this ratio will be only 1.75. Moreover, we have the impression that, unlike the dog where the infusion of glucose at a constant rate tends to produce a progressive increase in P_G, in man increased utilization or some other factor causes P_G to level off into a

TABLE I

Reproducibility of glucose Tm in normal subjects

SUBJECT	DATE	INULIN CLEARANCE	GLUCOSE Tm	GLUCOSE LOAD/T_G	Δ GLUCOSE Tm
		cc. per minute	mg. per minute		per cent
J. J.	November 7, 1940	134	313	1.33	
	November 11, 1940	140	313	1.05	±0.00
E. B.	September 16, 1940	112	293	1.07	
	September 30, 1940	128	287	1.30	−0.02
	November 9, 1940	112	277	1.26	−0.06
C. H.	September 23, 1940	136	290	1.54	
	November 4, 1940	129	290	2.41	±0.00
L. T.	September 20, 1940	91	282	1.18	
	September 20, 1940	100	270	1.33	−0.04
T. T.	November 13, 1940	166	536	1.51	
	November 13, 1940	170	543	1.43	+0.01
	November 13, 1940	173	526	1.17	−0.02
I. N.	January 3, 1941	96	266	1.33	
	January 3, 1941	99	257	1.50	−0.03
	January 3, 1941	98	266	1.66	±0.00
	January 3, 1941	108	271	1.90	+0.02
	February 5, 1941	99	265	1.15	±0.00

plateau, or even to fall, so that the rate of infusion must be constantly accelerated (from 1.0 up to 4 grams per minute) in order to maintain a steadily ascending curve and to reach plasma concentrations as high as 700 mg. per cent.

[4] The highest urine flow ever observed by us was reached inadvertently while endeavoring to attain a high load/T_G ratio; the urine flow rose to 41 cc. per minute for twenty minutes (P_G = 1400 mg. per cent) during which time the inulin U/P ratio was reduced to 3.5. There was moderate cyanosis and considerable subjective discomfort because of dehydration. During forced glycuresis (P_G = 500 to 600 mg. per cent) urine flows as high as 20 to 25 cc. per minute are not infrequent, but rarely exceed 30 cc. per minute (inulin U/P ratio = 4.0 to 5.0). Such a draft upon the body fluids cannot be sustained for long, though one individual (C.P., 10/27/39) was not incommoded by an average urine flow of 32 cc. for 50 minutes, in spite of an infusion rate of only 6 cc. per minute. In general, urine flows during Tm_G measurement range from 12 to 20 cc. per minute, with the inulin or mannitol U/P ratio ranging from 6.5 to 4.0. Equally high urine flows (20 to 30 cc.) may be obtained during Tm_D measurement, with inulin U/P ratios ranging down to 4.0, though here such extreme diuresis is much less frequent.

TABLE II

Glucose Tm and diodrast Tm under the action of adrenalin, hyperemia and caffeine

The per cent change produced by adrenalin, hyperemia or caffeine is calculated on the basis of the control observation (or the average control value where more than one is shown) immediately preceding the experimental datum in the table.

Columns 3, 4, 7 and 9 are corrected to 1.73 sq. m.; column 9 is corrected to 98.5°F. rectal temperature on the assumption that diodrast Tm increases 10 per cent for each degree (F.) of temperature.

SUBJECT	DATE	PLASMA CLEARANCE Inulin C_{IN}	Diodrast C_D	FILTRATION FRACTION	GLUCOSE LOAD/T_G	GLUCOSE T_m	DIODRAST LOAD/T_D	DIODRAST T_m	Δ DIODRAST CLEARANCE	Δ GLUCOSE T_m	Δ DIODRAST T_m	
		cc. per minute	cc. per minute			mg. per minute		mg. iodine per minute	per cent	per cent	per cent	
P. F.	5/19/38	139	852	16.3			4.55	57.6				Control
	5/30/38	134	604	22.2			2.39	58.7	−29		+2	Adrenalin
	5/25/38	143	1528				2.50	56.3	+79		−2	Hyperemia
J. C.	12/27/38	141	472	29.8			2.39	61.0				Adrenalin
	12/21/38	144	954	15.1			2.81	63.4	+102		+4	Hyperemia
F. A.	1/30/39	113	746	15.2			3.56	53.7				Control
	12/29/38	138	560	24.6			3.76	58.8	−25		+9	Adrenalin
	1/25/39	124	1270	9.8			2.61	53.4	+70		−1	Hyperemia
A. L.	2/17/39	131	854	15.4	1.79	282						Control
	2/17/39	120	542	22.2	1.70	299			−37	+6		Adrenalin
W. S.	2/10/39	148	697	21.2	1.72	338						Control
	2/10/39	139	555	25.1	1.64	360			−20	+6		Adrenalin
E. M.	3/ 1/39	129	666	19.4	1.74	344	2.99	48.7				Control
	1/26/39	128	808	15.8			3.97	45.8	+21		−6	Hyperemia
	3/ 8/39	111	847	13.2	1.81	332	8.15	44.5	+26	−3	−9	Hyperemia
	12/22/38	126	746				2.50	51.0	+12		+5	Hyperemia
J. J.	3/15/39	162	946	17.1	1.84	385	7.12	56.4				Control
	4/14/39	198			2.13	374						Control
	3/24/39	146	1655	8.8	1.79	416	16.4	54.1	+75	+10	−4	Hyperemia
	4/ 5/39	146	757	19.3	2.25	372	4.83	64.5	−20	−2	+14	Adrenalin
H. M.	6/ 2/39	150			1.79	431						Control
	6/ 2/39	140			1.88	450				+4		Adrenalin
	6/14/39	138			1.63	455	3.02	65.7				Control
	6/14/39	129			1.68	458	2.16	64.2		+1	−2	Adrenalin
	5/10/39	154	1090	13.5	1.61	400			−12			Hyperemia
J. Hu	2/13/39	128	714	17.9	1.30	319						Control
	2/13/39	138	602	22.9	1.18	316			−16	−1		Caffeine
	2/20/39	124	752	16.5	1.37	322						Control
	2/20/39	126			1.19	299	4.32	40.3				Control
	2/27/39	137	655	21.7	1.45	336	8.25	43.2	−13	+8	+7	Caffeine
	3/ 3/39	129	950	13.1	1.57	338	8.42	42.2	+26	+9	+5	Hyperemia
C. C.	5/15/39	181	705	25.7	1.27	415	4.98	64.3				Control
	5/29/39	141			1.53	417						Control
	6/29/39	134			1.91	349	4.02	63.7				Control
	6/29/39	161			2.18	342	3.40	64.2		−13	±0	Caffeine
	5/22/39	147	818	18.0	1.58	392	6.72	60.6	+16	−1	−5	Hyperemia
	6/ 7/39	147	930	15.8	1.92	390	5.78	63.6	+32	−1	−1	Hyperemia

TABLE II—*Continued*

SUBJECT	DATE	PLASMA CLEARANCE		FILTRATION FRACTION	GLUCOSE LOAD/T_G	GLUCOSE Tm	DIODRAST LOAD/T_D	DIODRAST Tm	Δ DIODRAST CLEARANCE	Δ GLUCOSE Tm	Δ DIODRAST Tm	
		Inulin C_{IN}	Diodrast C_D									
		cc. per minute	cc. per minute			mg. per minute		mg. iodine per minute	per cent	per cent	per cent	
R. D.	2/24/39	135	920		1.21	356	3.85	58.7				Control
	3/ 6/39	137	1302				9.45	46.2	+42		−21	Hyperemia
	6/ 9/39	117			1.25	351	2.06	59.8				Control
	6/ 9/39	140			1.10	377	1.85	54.0		+7	−10	Caffeine
	6/15/39	117					2.26	51.8				Control
	6/15/39	122					2.24	45.4			−12	Caffeine
J. B.	6/28/39	127			1.44	309	4.27	59.7				Control
	6/28/39	139			1.40	319	5.32	59.4		+3	−1	Caffeine
T. S.	10/18/39	156			1.74	344	2.02	57.5				Control
	10/18/39	157			1.73	394	1.73	55.4		+15	−4	Adrenalin
	10/25/39	138			1.77	317	2.58	57.0		−8		Control
C. P.	10/20/39	160			1.63	416	1.86	58.2				Control
	10/20/39	119			2.50	213	1.44	55.4		−49	−5	Adrenalin
	10/27/39	161			1.75	420	3.55	56.7				Control
	11/ 3/39	164	904		1.76	424						Control
P. M.	10/16/39	119			1.82	246	1.19	62.4				Control
	10/16/39	126			2.22	267	1.22	52.5		+9	−16	Adrenalin
	10/11/39	93			1.92	227	3.21	55.3				Control
	10/11/39	128			3.09	207	3.50	51.9		−9	−6	Caffeine
	10/23/39	114			1.74	257	2.89	59.4				Control

Even under these conditions U_GV may not exceed 0.25 grams per minute. The great capacity of the body to dispose of glucose by storage or utilization presents one of the chief difficulties in the glucose titration method.

In most of the control observations in Tables I and II the load/T_G ratio has not varied greatly in the several observations, (this difference being greater than 0.3 only in C. H., T. T., and I. N.), but a wider spread is available in the various experimental observations in Table II; since T_G did not change under the experimental conditions there recorded, we believe these data may be considered as supplementing the data in Table I, from which we infer that definitive Tm_G is generally reached in the normal kidney at a load/T_G ratio of 1.25, and that no increase in T_G is to be expected at higher levels.[5]

[5] In a previous report we believed that glucose reabsorption had a perceptible temperature coefficient, like the tubular excretion of diodrast (19). Subsequent observations have caused us to doubt this view; the question is not readily examined experimentally, but we feel that for the present it is advisable to omit temperature corrections and to present the data as observed. Consequently certain data on Tm_G from Table III of our previous paper (19) are again presented here, uncorrected for temperature, while other data in that table are excluded from the present report on the grounds that the load/T_G ratio is not high enough to insure saturation. The present data may be taken as replacing the previous table entirely.

3. Determination of definitive Tm_D

The elevation of the plasma concentration of diodrast to levels at which all tubules are saturated (load/T_D ratio greater than 2.0) is a relatively easy matter, but experience has taught us that the injection of large quantities of diodrast solution is apt to temporarily reduce Tm_D, probably by causing vasoconstriction of some of the renal arterioles. The reaction is unusual, however, if the priming injection of diodrast is administered slowly.

4. Independence of tubular reabsorption and tubular excretion

To answer the question whether tubular reabsorption (glucose) is physiologically independent of tubular excretion (diodrast), we have measured these terms both simultaneously and independently in several subjects. In no case have we found that either value is affected by saturation of the other system.[6] In view of the above fact, Tm_G and Tm_D may be determined simultaneously, as has been done in some instances in Table II. The double procedure is not recommended, however, since it offers opportunities for unanticipated complications.

5. The reproducibility of Tm_G and Tm_D, as examined by adrenalin, caffeine and pyrogenic hyperemia

The present section is an inquiry into the question of whether Tm_G and Tm_D are influenced by drugs which alter the effective renal blood flow, as measured by the diodrast clearance (see Table II). In such an examination it is desirable to have some knowledge of the extent to which these agents have altered the renal blood flow. Since saturation of the tubules with respect to the reabsorption of glucose does not interfere with the tubular excretion of diodrast, the diodrast clearance can be followed simultaneously with the measurement of Tm_G for eight to ten successive clearance periods, the drug being administered at the middle of the series. (Examples of this procedure are given in Table II in the observations on A. L., W. S., etc.) If no information is desired on the diodrast clearance, i.e., if the action of the drug on the renal blood flow is to be inferred from separate observations made under comparable conditions, Tm_D may similarly be followed throughout the "control" and "experimental" observations. (See H. M., June 14, 1939.) Or the "control" and "experimental" observations on Tm_D may be made on different occasions, as in the case of P. F., J. C., etc. This has been the invariable procedure in the study of pyrogenic hyperemia, since it was desirable to observe both the diodrast clearance and Tm_D during the hyperemic state, in order to determine to what extent the renal blood flow had been increased by the pyrogen.

Adrenalin. The action of adrenalin on the renal circulation in man has been

---

[6] Substances which are excreted by the tubules (phenol red, diodrast, hippuran and other hippuric acid derivatives (13)) do interfere with the simultaneous excretion of each other; while xylose (and galactose) interfere with the reabsorption of glucose (29). Since both the (glucose) reabsorptive and excretory process are probably localized in the proximal tubule, it appears that systems which are chemically independent of each other may be localized in the same nephron segment, and possibly in the same tubule cell.

discussed elsewhere (7). Adrenalin reduces the effective renal plasma flow by constriction of the efferent glomerular arterioles. The dose usually employed here has been 0.5 mg. subcutaneously plus 0.5 mg. intramuscularly, though occasionally where there was no marked effect on blood pressure a supplementary dose of 0.5 mg. intramuscularly has been given about twenty minutes later in order to maintain the action through the whole period of renal observation. The diodrast clearance was followed in P. F., F. A., W. S. and J. J. and was consistently reduced (-29, -25, -37, -20 and -20 per cent), confirming our previous experience.

$\Delta Tm_G = +6$, $+6$, -2, $+4$, $+1$, $+15$ (T. S.) and $+9$ per cent (average net $\Delta = +6$ per cent). The preponderance of changes in the positive direction might indicate that adrenalin increases the filtration rate in a few glomeruli in which this rate is normally too low to effect tubular saturation at the load/T_G ratios used, but the series as a whole shows that the proportion of such nephrons is small. It can certainly be concluded that adrenalin does not close any glomeruli, in spite of a marked reduction in total blood flow.

(Subject C. P. received a supplementary intramuscular injection of 0.5 mg. of adrenalin 20 minutes after the first divided dose, and showed a decrease of 49 per cent in Tm_G—i.e., a large number of glomeruli were apparently closed by the drug. Since the filtration rate dropped 26 per cent, it appears that widespread afferent constriction occurred. There were no exceptional objective symptoms and no subjective complaints. This is the only time a response of this type has occurred in many observations on adrenalin and we consider it atypical, at least for moderate doses.)

$\Delta Tm_D = +2$, $+9$, $+14$, -2, -4, -5 and -16 per cent (average net $\Delta =$ nil). Although two of these changes are large, they are in opposite directions, and the other changes are also inconsistent. We conclude, therefore, that adrenalin does not bring into or exclude from perfusion any substantial quantity of tubular tissue.

Caffeine. The xanthine derivatives have a complex effect upon the renal circulation; there is a delayed reduction in renal blood flow which appears to be an indirect effect of the drug upon the efferent glomerular arterioles, mediated perhaps through increased sympathetic tone; and there is generally a slow, progressive, but slight increase in filtration rate which, since the mean arterial pressure is not greatly increased, may represent slight dilatation of the afferent glomerular arterioles (7). Although theophylline is more popular in clinical use, partly because it has less central effect, caffeine is the substance which has been demonstrated to increase the glomerular circulation in cold-blooded animals and we have therefore used caffeine throughout this study. The dose has ranged from 1.0 gram intramuscularly and 1.0 gram intravenously of caffeine sodium benzoate down to half this amount. The diodrast clearance was followed in two instances only (both on J. Hu.), and showed a decrease (-16 and -13 per cent), while the filtration rate consistently increased ($+8$, $+9$, $+20$, $+4$, $+38$ and $+9$ per cent, average net change $= +15$ per cent), both results being in agreement with our previous study.

$\Delta Tm_G = -1$, $+8$, -13, $+7$, $+3$ and -9 per cent (average net $\Delta = -1$

per cent).   The failure of Tm_G to increase consistently at a time when the total
filtration rate is increased indicates that caffeine does not increase the filtration
rate in any significant number of glomeruli in which this rate is so low as to
prevent saturation of the tubules at the load/T_G ratio used.

$\Delta Tm_D = +7, \pm0, -10, -12, -1$ and -6 per cent (average net $\Delta = -8$
per cent).   Two of these results (-10 and -12 per cent) were obtained in a
subject R. D., in whom Tm_D has shown marked changes in control observations
(51.8 to 59.8), and we suspect that this is an example of spontaneous changes in
intrinsic tubular activity of unknown origin, such as are discussed in connection
with renal function in hypertensive subjects (19).   Excluding this subject, the
other changes are so slight as to indicate that caffeine does not disturb tubular
perfusion.

Hyperemia.   Renal hyperemia (7) was induced by the intravenous injection
of pyrogenic inulin of known potency (Lot No. 268).   In every case the subject
was premedicated with amidopyrine (10 grains every four hours for 16 to 24
hours before the test) in order to block autonomic disturbances other than the
renal response.   The diodrast clearance was followed in most instances and
generally increased markedly ($+79, +70, +21, +12, +75, +26, +16, +32$
and $+41$ per cent, with an extreme difference in J. C., as between adrenalin
and hyperemia, of $+102$ per cent).

$\Delta Tm_G = -3, +10, -12, +9, -1$ and -1 (average net $\Delta = +2$ per cent).
That Tm_G changes so little indicates that pyrogenic hyperemia (efferent arteriolar
dilatation) does not increase activity in any subactive glomeruli.

$\Delta Tm_D = -2, +4, -1, -6, -9, +5, -4, +5, -5, -1, -21$ per cent (average
net $\Delta = -3$ per cent).   The single large change (-21 per cent) is again in
R. D., and may reflect a spontaneous rather than an experimentally induced
change.   The slight changes in other instances indicate that renal hyperemia
does not bring under perfusion any unperfused tubules in the normal kidney.
(This is not the case in some subjects with essential hypertension (20).)

Discussion.   Were any appreciable number of glomeruli in the normal kidney
inactive, or prone to pass into a state of low activity by virtue of normal intermittency, we believe that one or all of these methods of examination would
have revealed changes in Tm_G of a much larger order of magnitude than those
observed.   It is true that in the case of both adrenalin ischemia and pyrogenic
hyperemia, the chief locus of action on the renal vascular tree appears to be
beyond the glomeruli, presumably in the efferent glomerular arterioles; and it is
possible that constriction of the efferent arteriole would not arrest filtration
in an otherwise active glomerulus, while efferent dilatation would not permit
restoration of activity in a previously inactive glomerulus; but it is difficult to
believe that such marked changes in total renal blood flow would fail to disturb
a pattern of intermittent activity involving any large number of glomeruli,
were such intermittent activity present.   The argument is more cogent in the
case of caffeine, which increases the total filtration rate: the failure of this drug
to increase Tm_G is very strong evidence against intermittent glomerular activity.

Diodrast Tm refers to the number of "active" tubules which are perfused at any moment. We have elsewhere (35) remarked on the possible importance of the circulation of interstitial fluid in the perfusion of the tubules (see also p. 94); if this presupposition is credited, it is perhaps not to be expected that marked changes in renal blood flow would result in significant changes in the perfusion of tubular tissue, since the continued circulation of interstitial fluid would tend to maintain tubular perfusion even where some glomeruli were inactive. But it is equally possible that the perfusion of the tubules is strictly dependent on the perfusion of the glomeruli, and that our failure to modify Tm_D is contingent upon the circumstance that glomerular activity is uniformly maintained under all the above conditions.

In any case, the above results, in showing that the number of nephrons reabsorbing glucose at moderate load/T_G ratios is not increased by circumstances which greatly increase glomerular pressure (adrenalin and caffeine) or total renal blood flow (hyperemia), controvert the idea, carried into mammalian physiology from observations on cold-blooded animals, that any significant number of glomeruli are inactive at any moment.

III. COMPARISON OF Tm_G AND Tm_D IN NORMAL SUBJECTS

The foregoing studies, carried out under conditions representing the most vigorous vascular changes readily induced in the human kidney, afford increased confidence in the significance of the data obtained by the use of the glucose and diodrast saturation methods. The reproducibility of Tm_G and Tm_D is such that we may proceed on the premise that the intrinsic activity of both the reabsorptive and excretory mechanisms of the tubules is essentially stable and amenable to adequate measurement. (The reader is cautioned that certain procedures can of course close the glomeruli, or acutely reduce perfusion of the tubules, and a subsequent section of this paper is devoted to precautions which must be taken in this respect.)

This intrinsic stability leads to the expectation that a comparison of the two saturation methods in the diseased kidney may afford information on the effects of disease on specific tubular processes.[7] For this comparison a knowledge of the normal statistical parameters is of course necessary, and consequently the available normal data are summarized in Table III. Other pertinent data on the filtration rate (C_{IN}), diodrast clearance (C_D), etc., are included for completeness.

The data on normal subjects in Table III are divided into the "old series" presented in a previous paper (19), the "new series" here presented for the first time, and a "combined series" in which all data are treated together.[8] In the

---

[7] One of course cannot generalize from the reabsorption of glucose to the reabsorption of chloride, water or other substances, since entirely different reabsorptive mechanisms are involved; nor from the excretion of diodrast to the excretion of other substances which may be handled by wholly independent mechanisms. As renal physiology increasingly develops quantitative methods and modes of thought the reiteration of these qualifications becomes increasingly superfluous.

[8] We are greatly indebted to Mr. Charles Sternheel for the statistical analysis of the new and combined series.

TABLE III

Glucose Tm and diodrast Tm in normal subjects

Each datum in columns 5, 6, 7, 8 and 9 represents the average of three or more clearance periods, and is corrected to 1.73 sq. m.; column 8 is corrected to 98.5°F.

SUBJECT	AGE	SUR-FACE AREA	DATE	PLASMA CLEARANCE Inulin	PLASMA CLEARANCE Diodrast	EFFECTIVE BLOOD FLOW	DIODRAST Tm	GLUCOSE Tm	INULIN CLEARANCE/ GLUCOSE Tm	DIODRAST CLEARANCE/ GLUCOSE Tm	GLUCOSE Tm/DIODRAST Tm	INULIN CLEARANCE/ DIODRAST Tm	DIODRAST CLEARANCE/ DIODRAST Tm	INULIN CLEARANCE/ DIODRAST CLEARANCE
		sq. m.		cc. per minute	cc. per minute	cc. per minute	mg. iodine per minute	mg. per minute						
Men														
W. S.	48	1.52	2/10/39	148	697	1200		338	0.438	2.06				21.2
J. Hu	39	1.85	2/13/39	128	714	1210	40.3	315	0.406	2.27	7.82	3.18	17.7	17.9
A. L.	42	1.88	2/17/39	131	854	1690		282	0.465	3.03				15.3
E. Mc	50	1.84	3/ 1/39	129	666	1044	45.1	342	0.377	1.95	7.58	2.86	14.8	19.4
J. J.	28	1.65	3/15/39	162	946	1505	58.3	380	0.426	2.49	6.52	2.78	16.2	17.1
C. C.	42	1.77	5/15/39	150	705	1320	64.0	383	0.392	1.84	5.99	2.34	11.0	21.3
R. D.	28	1.98	6/ 9/39	117			56.8	354	0.331		6.23	2.06		
H. M.	34	1.81	6/14/39	144			65.7	443	0.325		6.74	2.19		
J. B.	45	1.48	6/28/39	127			59.7	309	0.411		5.18	2.13		
P. M.	36	1.72	10/16/39	109			59.0	243	0.448		4.12	1.85		
T. S.	37	1.70	10/18/39	147			57.3	330	0.445		5.76	2.57		
C. P.	34	1.67	10/20/39	162			57.5	420	0.386		7.30	2.82		
T. T.	32	1.62	12/ 4/40	166	704	1043	53.4	536	0.310	1.31	10.04	3.11	13.2	23.6
W. F.	31	1.77	12/18/40	136	654	1063	48.0	477	0.285	1.37	9.94	2.83	13.6	20.8
I. N.	34	1.53	1/ 3/41	100	389	635	32.0	269	0.372	1.45	8.41	3.13	12.2	25.7
P. H.	52	1.80	1/13/41	152	784	1387	44.1	380	0.400	2.06	8.62	3.45	17.8	19.4
W. Mc	40	1.77	1/27/41	173	943	1685		580	0.298	1.63				18.3
J. Bg	49	1.76	3/21/41	112	674	1262	44.1	269	0.416	2.51	6.10	2.54	15.3	16.6
W. O.	48	1.88	3/31/41	128	845	1496	42.5	380	0.337	2.22	8.94	3.01	19.9	15.1
H. B.	58	1.77	4/ 2/41	114	649	1152	47.2	437	0.261	1.49	9.26	2.42	13.8	17.6
M. D.	60	1.73	4/ 7/41	138	664	1072	56.4	406	0.340	1.64	7.20	2.45	11.8	20.8
J. L.	39	1.91	4/14/41	116	592	1047	49.6	396	0.293	1.49	7.98	2.34	11.9	19.6
J. W.	45	1.73	5/26/41	152	876	1753	49.8	380	0.400	2.31	7.63	3.05	17.6	17.4
J. R.	39	1.59	6/16/41	123	578	1040	56.0	353	0.348	1.64	6.30	2.20	10.3	21.3

Present series, normal men

	Inulin	Diodrast	EFF. BLOOD FLOW	DIODRAST Tm	GLUCOSE Tm	INULIN/ GLUCOSE Tm	DIODRAST/ GLUCOSE Tm	GLUCOSE Tm/ DIODRAST Tm	INULIN/ DIODRAST Tm	DIODRAST/ DIODRAST Tm	INULIN/ DIODRAST
n	24	18	18	21	24	24	18	21	21	15	18
Mean	136	719	1256	51.8	375	0.371	1.93	7.32	2.63	14.5	0.193
σ	19.3	134.9	280.3	8.30	79.7	0.0563	0.460	1.51	0.422	2.77	0.0266
σm	3.94	31.8	66.1	1.81	16.3	0.0115	0.108	0.330	0.092	0.715	0.0063
r						0.656	0.323	0.235	0.430	0.366	
$100\,\sigma/m$	14.2	18.8	22.3	16.0	21.2	15.2	23.8	20.6	16.0	19.1	13.8

Original series, normal men

	Inulin	Diodrast	EFF. BLOOD FLOW	DIODRAST Tm				GLUCOSE Tm/ DIODRAST Tm	INULIN/ DIODRAST Tm	DIODRAST/ DIODRAST Tm	INULIN/ DIODRAST
n	54	43	43	26				26	19		43
Mean	130	688	1189	53.3				2.57	13.6		0.189
σ	21.7	135.3	242.4	9.1				0.28	1.4		0.024
σm	2.96	20.6	36.9	1.8				0.055	0.32		0.0036
r								0.77	0.77		
$100\,\sigma/m$	16.7	19.7	20.4	17.1				10.9	10.3		12.7

TABLE III—*Concluded*

| SUBJECT | AGE | SURFACE AREA | DATE | PLASMA CLEARANCE | | EFFECTIVE BLOOD FLOW | DIODRAST T_m | GLUCOSE T_m | INULIN CLEARANCE/GLUCOSE T_m | DIODRAST CLEARANCE/GLUCOSE T_m | GLUCOSE T_m/DIODRAST T_m | INULIN CLEARANCE/DIODRAST T_m | DIODRAST CLEARANCE/DIODRAST T_m | INULIN CLEARANCE/DIODRAST CLEARANCE |
				Inulin	Diodrast									
				cc. per minute	cc. per minute	cc. per minute	mg. iodine per minute	mg. per minute						

Combined series, normal men

n				67	61	61	40	24	24	18	21	40	34	61
Mean				131	697	1209	51.8	79.7	0.371	1.93	7.32	2.63	14.0	0.190
σ				21.5	135.9	255.9	8.73	16.3	0.0563	0.460	1.51	0.344	2.16	0.0244
σ_m				2.63	17.4	32.8	1.38	16.3	0.0115	0.108	0.330	0.054	0.370	0.0031
r									0.656	0.323	0.235	0.681	0.633	
100σ/m				16.4	19.5	21.2	16.8	21.2	15.2	23.8	20.6	13.1	15.4	12.8

Women

		sq. m.												
J. Ha	50	1.72	12/ 2/40	135	567	886		445	0.303	1.27				23.8
H. P.	16	1.73	3/24/41	116	682	1137	35.8	349	0.333	1.95	9.75	3.24	19.0	17.0
M. M.	31	1.49	3/28/41	104	344	565	24.0	280	0.372	1.23	11.66	4.34	14.3	30.2
A. C.	45	1.68	6/ 2/41	123	724	1234	40.9	280	0.439	2.59	6.85	3.01	17.7	17.0
V. P.	26	1.63	6/ 4/41	115	650	1054	40.1	283	0.407	2.30	7.06	2.87	16.2	17.7
C. V.	35	1.73	6/23/41	106	537	926	34.7	212	0.500	2.53	6.11	3.06	15.5	19.7
E. B.	24	1.53	9/16/40	117				283	0.414					
L. T.	51	1.57	9/20/40	92				276	0.333					
C. H.	33	1.44	9/23/40	134				290	0.463					
R. P.	55	1.84	8/ 2/40	106				319	0.332					
J. J.	17	1.75	8/ 7/41					313	0.451					

Present series, normal women

n				10	6	6	5	11	11	6	5	5	5	6
Mean				115	584	967	35.1	303	0.395	1.98	8.29	3.30	16.5	0.209
σ				12.8	124.9	215.1	6.04	55.3	0.0617	0.554	2.09	0.531	1.65	0.0478
σ_m				4.05	51.0	87.8	2.70	16.7	0.0186	0.226	0.934	0.237	0.738	0.0195
r									0.048	0.135	0.069	0.818	0.944	
100 σ/m				11.1	21.4	22.2	17.2	18.3	15.6	28.0	25.2	16.1	10.0	22.9

Original series, normal women

n				11	11	11	9					9	9	11
Mean				118.7	600.4	996	46.7					2.54	12.8	0.198
σ				17.5	87.0	162.7	8.5					0.28	1.52	0.014
σ_m				5.28	26.2	49.1	2.83					0.125	0.68	0.0042
100 σ/m				14.7	14.5	16.3	18.2					11.0	11.9	7.1

Combined series, normal women

n				21	17	17	14	11	11	6	5	14	14	17
Mean				117	594	982	42.6	303	0.395	1.98	8.29	2.81	14.2	0.202
σ				15.6	102.4	184.4	9.46	55.3	0.0617	0.554	2.09	0.555	2.36	0.0310
σ_m				3.40	24.8	44.7	2.53	16.7	0.0186	0.226	0.934	0.148	0.631	0.0075
r									0.048	0.135	0.069	0.674	0.603	
100 σ/m				13.3	17.2	18.8	22.2	18.2	15.6	28.0	25.2	19.7	16.6	15.3

statistical analysis our old data on Tm_G are wholly replaced by those of the present paper, for reasons cited earlier; and since each subject is counted only once, certain duplications in C_{IN} and Tm_D are omitted, chiefly from among those subjects who appeared in our previously published Table III (19).

Examination of the summaries in our present Table III shows that the means of the new and old series are in good agreement, especially among the men where the numbers of individuals are larger. The correlation coefficient, r, between C_{IN} and Tm_D and between C_D and Tm_D is lower among men in the new series, but remains good in the combined series in both sexes, bearing out the usefulness

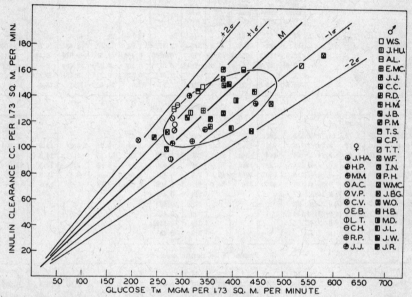

FIG. 1. Inulin Clearance (C_{IN} or Filtration Rate) in Normal Subjects, Related to Glucose Tm (Tm_G or Maximal Rate of Glucose Reabsorption).

The statistical background, M, is the mean ratio C_{IN}/Tm_G, ± multiples of the standard deviation. The ellipse is calculated (20, see also note at end of this paper) to contain 70 per cent of the observations, and actually contains 71 per cent.

of Tm_D as an index of the quantity of functional tissue to which to refer C_{IN} and C_D.

With the increase in the number of data on women, it has seemed desirable to separate the two sexes and use the specific sex data for future reference, especially since in every case the means are significantly smaller in women than in men. In all statistical references in this paper the appropriate sex standards, as cited under the combined series, are used.

One major purpose of this study concerns the relation of Tm_G to other renal functions, and it will be observed in Table III that this term has a significantly positive correlation (0.656) only with C_{IN} among the men, the correlation with Tm_D and C_D being so low (0.323 and 0.235) as to be questionable. Among the women, C_{IN} and Tm_G show no correlation, but we believe that this may be fortuitously related to the small sample.   As the reader will see in Figure 1, both terms have a relatively narrow dispersion, which circumstance contributes some uncertainty to the coefficient of correlation; while the dispersion in the case of women is even narrower.   In neither case is the series large enough to warrant confident conclusions, but the data indicate that Tm_G is positively correlated with C_{IN} in men (and by inference we believe this to be true of women) (fig. 1): *i.e.*, the tubular reabsorptive capacity is roughly proportional to the filtration rate.

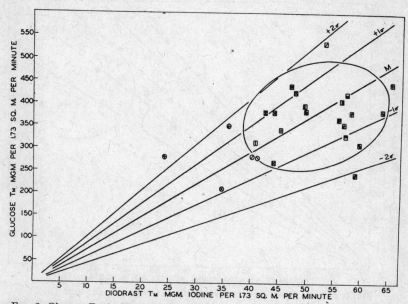

FIG. 2. Glucose Tm in Normal Subjects, Related to Diodrast Tm (Maximal Rate of Tubular Excretion).
The statistical background, M, is the mean ratio Tm_G/Tm_D ± multiples of the standard deviation.   The ellipse is calculated to contain 70 per cent of the observations, and actually contains 72 per cent.

The correlation between Tm_G and Tm_D is relatively poor: *i.e.*, the tubular reabsorptive capacity bears little or no relation to the tubular excretory capacity, as is shown in Figure 2.

A positive correlation between C_{IN} and Tm_G is rather to be anticipated, in view of the functional relationship which, in the interests of glucose conservation, we may expect to find between any glomerulus and its nephron. *A priori*, there is no reason to expect that glucose reabsorption would have any functional relationship to renal blood flow or tubular excretion, and hence the poorer correlation of Tm_G with C_D and Tm_D is not surprising.   This poor correlation shows that the reabsorptive and excretory activities of a tubule, even where these are probably localized in the same segment, may be developed to quite different functional levels, and reveals the precariousness of judging tubular functional capacity by one index, and especially by cytological appearance.

IV. COMPARISON OF Tm_G AND Tm_D IN HYPERTENSIVE SUBJECTS

In our previous paper on renal function in subjects with essential hypertension (20), we recorded our conclusion that during the progress of this disease the excretory capacity of the tubules for diodrast is impaired, leading to a reduction in Tm_D. Since in some subjects the ratio C_{IN}/Tm_D had values far in excess of

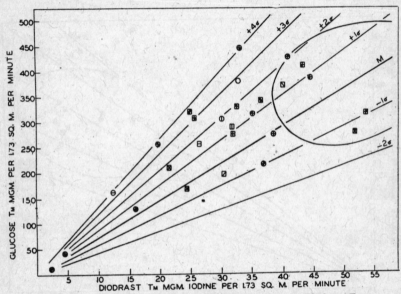

FIG. 3. Glucose Tm in Hypertensive Subjects, Related to Diodrast Tm

The statistical background is the *normal mean* (M) ratio Tm_G/Tm_D, ± multiples of the standard deviation, as shown in Figure 2. Most of the observations are *low* in respect to the normal value of Tm_D, but normal in respect to the value of Tm_G. Hence 74 per cent fall above the mean ratio, M. I.e., Tm_D may be decreased markedly in hypertensive subjects, while Tm_G is essentially normal. The term "impotent" has been used to describe tubules which have lost the power of excreting diodrast, but which remain connected to functional glomeruli: the trend depicted here indicates that such "impotent" tubules can reabsorb glucose.

normal, we inferred that this loss of excretory capacity might occur without obliteration of the glomerulus or occlusion of the tubule in a certain fraction of nephrons, leading to the formation of what we called "impotent" nephrons. (We recognized that increased glomerular pressure associated with elevated blood pressure could produce the same effect, and that there was available in the study referred to no certain means of differentiating these factors; nevertheless the general relations of the data led us to place the emphasis on tubular impotence rather than increased glomerular pressure.)

It is of special interest then to observe the relative values of Tm_G and Tm_D

in hypertensive subjects. Data pertinent to this question are given in Table IV and Figures 3 and 4. These data show that:

1) In the hypertensive kidney Tm_D may suffer marked reduction while Tm_G tends to remain within the normal limits of 200–450 mg. per minute. This is well displayed by the scatter diagram of Figure 3, which is to be compared with Figure 2 for the normal distribution. It will be seen from Figure 3 that the ratio Tm_G/Tm_D for most subjects lies well above the normal mean (M), in consequence primarily of a reduction in Tm_D rather than in consequence of an increase in Tm_G

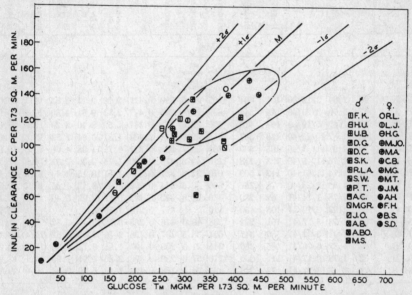

FIG. 4. Inulin Clearance in Hypertensive Subjects, Related to Glucose Tm

The statistical background is the *normal mean* (M) ratio C_{IN}/Tm_G, $\pm$ standard deviation, as shown in Figure 1. Although both C_{IN} and Tm_G tend to fall below the mean normal values, the ratio C_{IN}/Tm_G is maintained at its normal value, indicating that Tm_G is not specifically affected by the disease, but is decreased only in consequence of reduction of C_{IN}. I.e., as glomeruli are deleted from the kidney by arteriolar or glomerular lesions, the attached tubules necessarily drop out of glucose reabsorption, but glucose reabsorption *per se* is not impaired by hypertensive disease.

In two subjects (S. W. and P. T.) the filtration rate is excessively low, perhaps reflecting thickening of the glomerular membranes or some other impediment to filtration, not typically present in the other subjects.

2) Tm_G and C_{IN} maintain an almost *precisely normal proportional ratio* in the hypertensive kidney, as is shown by Figure 4, from which fact we infer that Tm_G is reduced only if the filtration rate is reduced; *i.e.*, glucose reabsorption is not specifically impaired in hypertensive disease, and Tm_G is reduced only when the glomerulus of a nephron is obliterated by vascular changes and the attached tubule is passively cut off from reabsorptive activity. The alternative explanation, that specific impairment of tubular reabsorptive capacity is primary but that the filtration rate is simultaneously reduced to a proportional extent, so as

TABLE IV

Glucose Tm and diodrast Tm in hypertensive subjects

Each datum in columns 5, 6, 7, 8 and 9 represents the average of three or more clearance periods. Columns 5, 6 7, 8 and 9 are corrected to 1.73 sq. m.; column 8 is corrected to 98.5°F.

SUBJECT	AGE	SUR-FACE AREA	DATE	PLASMA CLEARANCE Inulin	PLASMA CLEARANCE Diodrast	EFFECTIVE BLOOD FLOW	DIODRAST Tm	GLUCOSE Tm	INULIN CLEARANCE/ GLUCOSE Tm	DIODRAST CLEARANCE/ GLUCOSE Tm	GLUCOSE Tm/DIODRAST Tm	INULIN CLEARANCE/ DIODRAST Tm	DIODRAST CLEARANCE/ DIODRAST Tm	FILTRATION FRACTION
		sq. m.		*cc. per minute*	*cc. per minute*	*cc. per minute*	*mg. iodine per minute*	*mg. per minute*						
Men
F. K.	21	1.64	3/13/39	121	604	1105	31.6	290	0.417	2.08	9.17	3.83	19.1	20.0
H. U.	47	1.70	3/29/39	114	544	899	26.5	255	0.447	2.13	9.61	4.30	20.5	20.9
U. B.	37	1.87	5/19/39	104	416	695	32.5	273	0.381	1.52	8.40	3.20	12.8	25.0
D. G.	48	1.82	10/25/40	136	567	1053	53.7	314	0.433	1.81	5.84	2.53	10.6	24.0
D. C.	58	1.97	11/ 3/40	105	530	888	25.7	308	0.341	1.72	11.98	4.08	20.6	19.8
S. K.	46	1.76	11/ 8/40	123	718	1116	43.3	410	0.300	1.75	9.46	2.84	16.9	17.1
R. La	66	1.74	11/11/40	112	500	910	32.6	331	0.338	1.51	10.15	3.43	15.3	22.4
S. W.	61	1.65	11/29/40	71	367	666	36.5	344	0.206	1.07	9.42	1.95	10.1	19.3
P. T.	60	1.76	1/24/41	62	280	470	24.9	322	0.192	0.87	12.92	2.49	11.2	22.1
A. C.	66	1.93	2/19/41	103	450	810		377	0.273	1.19				22.9
M. Gr	64	1.95	3/17/41	101	271	538	40.0	376	0.268	0.72	9.40	2.52	6.8	37.2
J. O.	43	1.94	3/12/41	80	347	691	30.5	197	0.406	1.76	6.46	2.62	11.4	23.1
A. B.	62	1.82	6/ 6/41	85	386	645	21.5	209	0.407	1.85	9.72	3.95	17.9	22.0
A. Bo	32	1.78	10/17/41	111	802	1710	57.0	280	0.396	2.86	4.91	1.95	14.1	13.9
M. S.	26	2.03	10/27/41	72	246	499	24.5	168	0.428	1.46	6.86	2.94	10.0	29.2
Women
R. L.	49	1.29	3/10/39	145	570	976	32.6	381	0.381	1.50	11.68	4.44	17.5	25.4
L. J.	44	1.57	3/27/39	120	471	785	30.1	306	0.392	1.54	10.17	3.99	15.6	25.5
H. G.	34	1.73	4/19/39	63	207	362	12.3	162	0.389	1.28	13.17	5.12	16.8	30.4
M. Jo	37	1.62	5/ 1/39	114	556	785	38.6	276	0.413	2.01	7.15	2.95	14.4	20.1
M. A.	32	1.53	11/ 6/39	151	490	823	40.9	427	0.354	1.15	10.44	3.69	12.0	30.8
C. B.	55	1.60	2/21/41	141			33.2	446	0.316		13.43	4.25		
M. G.	41	1.85	2/17/41	140			44.7	385	0.363		8.61	3.13		
M. T.	34	1.54	3/ 3/41	127	579	984	35.1	316	0.402	1.83	9.00	3.62	16.5	22.0
J. M.	56	1.61	3/14/41	91	375	744	19.8	256	0.355	1.47	12.92	4.60	18.9	24.2
B. G.	40	1.64	10/15/41	89	485	840	34.7	242	0.368	2.00	6.98	2.56	14.0	18.3
A. H.	41	1.69	10/29/41	23	71	101	4.4	40	0.575	1.78	9.10	5.22	16.1	32.4
F. H.	49	1.60	10/31/41	10	34	47	2.3	12	0.833	2.83	5.22	4.35	14.8	29.4
B. S.	44	2.05	11/28/41	88	357	540	37.0	217	0.405	1.65	5.86	2.38	9.7	24.6
S. D.	60	1.56	12/19/41	45	216	437	16.0	129	0.349	1.67	8.06	2.81	13.5	20.8
A. M.	52	2.00	2/16/42	71	415	692	28.8	211	0.336	1.97	7.33	2.46	14.4	17.1

to maintain a normal C_{IN}/Tm_G' ratio, seems less plausible since it requires a physiologically improbable coincidence.

The persistence of Tm_G when Tm_D is impaired is confirmatory evidence that our previous interpretation of the elevated C_{IN}/Tm_D ratio in hypertensive subjects is correct: namely, that nephrons which have in some measure lost the capacity to excrete diodrast are continuing to convey glomerular filtrate to the urine. Where, in particular subjects, C_{IN}/Tm_D is above normal, Tm_G/Tm_D is likewise above·normal. Our choice of the term "impotent" to describe such non-excretory nephrons may be questioned since by the present demonstration they can still reabsorb glucose and probably other substances, but we think the term will continue to be useful until further data on specific functional attributes are available.

In résumé, in hypertensive disease the tubular excretory capacity for diodrast, as measured by Tm_D, is impaired, without an equal impairment in the reabsorptive capacity for glucose, as measured by Tm_G. In the earlier stages of the disease the filtration rate apparently is not affected, though ultimately arteriolar and capillary lesions do impair the filtration bed and in proportion as this is obliterated Tm_G is reduced below normal values simply because of glomerular destruction. In the terminal stages of the disease all functions may be reduced to vestigial levels.

The reduction in Tm_D appears to be the most characteristic impairment of renal function in essential hypertension, and the question arises as to the possible significance of this reduction in the etiology of the disease, especially since the evidence on man argues against the primacy of renal ischemia (6, 14, 17, 18, 20, 36, 40, 42). It is impossible to look upon the tubular excretion of such artificial compounds as diodrast and hippuran (iodohippuric acid) as interesting teleologic paradoxes. In unpublished observations we have found that the naturally occurring hippuric acid, phenylaceturic acid and related compounds are excreted in a parallel manner (see 13) and we lean to the view that tubular excretion is a terminal step in a renal metabolic sequence, perhaps involving the conjugation of difficultly catabolizable aromatic residues such as benzoic and phenylacetic acids, and that a reduction in Tm_D may reflect a deficit in renal metabolic processes anterior to the process of excretion itself. In this connection increased interest attaches to the demonstration that Tm_D in dogs is reduced by hypophysectomy (47) and increased by large doses of testosterone (43) and vitamin A (Bing, unpublished observations) since by this evidence at least one process in renal metabolism is demonstrated to be related to factors outside the kidney. It remains to be discovered, however, whether the impairment of renal metabolism which is reflected in a reduction of Tm_D is causally related to the hypertensive process or whether the impairment is but one of the many degenerative effects of the disease.

V. THE TITRATION OF THE KIDNEYS WITH GLUCOSE AND DIODRAST

The examination of the kidneys by the simple determination of Tm_G and Tm_D is deficient for finer observations, in that it neglects the *load* of glucose or diodrast at which observations are made: the higher this load, the greater must be the decrease in glomerular filtration or tubular perfusion before a reabsorptive or excretory unit will cease to contribute to the sum-total of tubular activity; while the load itself is dependent upon two terms, the plasma concentration of glucose or diodrast, as the case may be, and the volume of carrier, *i.e.*, glomerular filtrate or peritubular perfusion fluid. This deficiency can be circumvented by "titrating" the kidneys with glucose or diodrast: *i.e.*, by progressively raising the plasma concentration of these substances between critical physiologic levels, it is possible to saturate various reabsorptive or excretory "units" in inverse order to the relative volume of carrier which they receive, until all are saturated and definitive Tm_G or Tm_D is reached. From the titration curve so obtained the volume of carrier distributed to these various "units" can be stated in either relative or absolute terms.

The following section is devoted to the development of this titration method and its application to the normal and hypertensive kidney.

1. Glucose titration

The following premises are erected:

(A) The phenomenon of a maximal glucose reabsorptive capacity, as observed in the overall activity of the two kidneys, reflects a similar quantitative limitation in every tubule: *i.e.*, every tubule reabsorbs all the glucose presented to it by its glomerulus until the load is exactly equal to its maximal reabsorptive capacity; when the load exceeds this capacity, the excess glucose is excreted in the urine.[9]

(B) The status of individual nephrons with respect to filtration rate and maximal glucose reabsorptive capacity remains unchanged during the period required for the completion of titration.[10]

Equation (*1*) (page 61), restated for individual nephrons in terms of the above premises, supplies the starting point for the following analysis. For individual nephrons (or functionally homogeneous categories of nephrons) the filtration rate may be indicated by c_{in}, the rate of glucose reabsorption by t, and the maximal reabsorptive capacity by tm.[11] Since a common stream of plasma supplies all glomeruli, p_g will be essentially identical for all nephrons and identical with P_G, the concentration of glucose in arterial plasma; c_{in} will, however, differ in various nephrons in consequence of differences in size and glomerular pressure; while tm will differ in various nephrons if for no other reason than be-

---

[9] It is here implied that there is negligible splay in the titration curve of any individual nephron, an implication supported by the relatively small splay in the titration curve of the entire kidneys, as shown in Figure 7.

[10] The necessity of maintaining the *status quo* throughout the process of titration is obvious and, since two to three hours are required to obtain a complete titration curve, the method in its present form is not adapted to the examination of the transient action of drugs, but is more suitable to the examination of the normal and diseased kidney under basal conditions, as applied here.

[11] The subscript g will be omitted from t_g and tm_g, but it is to be understood so long as we are dealing with glucose reabsorption, in order to differentiate these terms from the same terms used in Part V, section 3, for describing diodrast excretion.

cause the proximal segment[12] does not in all nephrons have the same size and length. In any particular nephron, the critical concentration of glucose required to just effect saturation of the tubule will vary directly as the maximal reabsorptive capacity of that tubule, and inversely as the rate of filtration in the glomerulus; so, generally, among a large number of nephrons those with the largest filtration rate per unit reabsorptive capacity, i.e., the largest c_{in}/tm ratio, will saturate at the lowest level of P_G, while those with the lowest c_{in}/tm ratio will require the highest level of P_G to effect saturation. Only those nephrons in which the ratio c_{in}/tm is identical will saturate at the same value of P_G.

The ratio c_{in}/tm may be designated as "glomerular activity," and indicated by r, since it expresses the rate of filtration (cc. per min.) in the glomerulus of a particular nephron, relative to the quantity of reabsorptive tissue in the tubule of that nephron, as measured by the maximal rate of glucose reabsorption (mg. per min.).[13]

We may speak of all nephrons which have, within practical limits of determination, the same c_{in}/tm ratio, as belonging to a "category" in respect to glomerular activity. The various nephrons in a "category" may have different absolute values of c_{in} or tm; these absolute values cannot be determined by the titration method, which reveals only differences in the ratio of these terms

The following tems are used in the mathematical analysis of the titration curve:

T_G = Total tubular reabsorption of glucose (mg. per min.).

Tm_G = Maximal value of T_G.

P_G = Plasma concentration of glucose (mg. per cc.).

C_{IN} = Glomerular filtration rate (cc. per min.).[14]

U_GV = Rate of excretion of glucose (mg. per min.).

The next five terms are applicable in principle either to a unit of reabsorptive tissue (i.e., a single nephron), or to an experimentally measured category of units having the same glomerular activity.

$\overline{c_{in}}$ = Rate of filtration in an unsaturated nephron (cc. per min.).

c_{in} = Rate of filtration in a saturated nephron (cc. per min.).

t = Rate of glucose reabsorption in an unsaturated nephron (mgm. per min.).

[12] It is demonstrated by the recent work of Walker, Bott, Oliver and MacDowell (41) on the mammalian nephron, that the reabsorption of glucose is a function of the proximal tubule.

[13] The reader will note that any reference to glomerular activity implies one or another standard of reference, such as the filtration rate in cc. per single glomerulus, or per unit of glomerular volume, diameter or area of filtering surface, etc. The present method of examination functionally relates the *volume* of glomerular filtrate to the *maximal glucose reabsorptive capacity* of the attached nephron.

[14] The term C_{IN} is usefully established for describing the filtration rate and is used in all equations here even though in much of the work mannitol was substituted for inulin. Wherever mannitol was used the fact is either stated in the text or the filtration rate is described as the mannitol clearance, C_M, in the legend.

tm = Rate of glucose reabsorption in a saturated nephron (mgm. per min.).

r = Glomerular activity (c_{in}/tm) in a particular nephron.

tm/Tm_G = Size of a category having a particular glomerular activity, expressed as a fraction of the entire tubular reabsorptive mass.

R = Total glomerular activity (C_{IN}/Tm_G) in the entire kidneys (which is also equal to the *mean* value of c_{in}/tm).

R_{normal} = Average value of mean glomerular activity in normal subjects.

Let it be supposed that P_G has been progressively raised from low levels, where no nephrons are saturated, to a level $P_{G'}$, at which an appreciable number of nephrons having a high glomerular activity are just saturated. The kidney is now nominally divided into two portions, one portion, a, in which all the nephrons are saturated, and a residuum, b, in which no nephron is saturated. For the portion, a,

$$(3) \qquad\qquad P_{G'}\, \Sigma c_{in} = \Sigma tm$$

where Σc_{in} and Σtm are, respectively, equal to the sum of c_{in} and tm in all nephrons considered as saturating at $P_{G'}$.

Now let P_G be raised to $P_{G''}$, a value sufficiently high to cause the nephrons in a to excrete a measurable quantity of glucose, but not high enough to saturate any nephrons in b. At $P_{G''}$, all the glucose filtered in a in excess of Σtm will appear in the urine; and, since no glucose will be excreted by the unsaturated nephrons in b, the increment in glucose excretion ($\Delta U_G V$) will be equal to $(P_{G''} - P_{G'})\Sigma c_{in}$. Writing $(P_{G''} - P_{G'}) = \Delta P_G$,

$$(4) \qquad\qquad \Sigma c_{in} = \frac{\Delta U_G V}{\Delta P_G}$$

The total filtration rate, C_{IN}, is the sum of the filtration rate in the saturated portion, ΔC_{in}, plus that in the unsaturated portion, $\Sigma C_{\overline{in}}$:

$$(5) \qquad\qquad C_{IN} = \Sigma c_{in} + \Sigma c_{\overline{in}}$$

The total rate of glucose reabsorption, T_G, is the sum of the rate of reabsorption in the saturated portion, Σtm, and in the unsaturated portion, Σt:

$$(6) \qquad\qquad T_G = \Sigma tm + \Sigma t$$

Σt is the rate of glucose reabsorption in the unsaturated portion:

$$(7) \qquad\qquad \Sigma t = P_{G'} \Sigma c_{\overline{in}} = P_{G'}(C_{IN} - \Sigma c_{in})$$

Hence from (4) and (6)

$$(8) \qquad\qquad \Sigma tm = T_{G'} - P_{G'} \left(C_{IN} - \frac{\Delta U_G V}{\Delta P_G} \right)$$

Since C_{IN} and Tm_G differ in various subjects, it is convenient for graphical comparison to express the titration curve in the universal terms of T_G/Tm_G

and $P_G C_{IN}/Tm_G$, as in all the Figures in this paper: to which end we may write $\Sigma\overline{c_{in}} = \dfrac{\Delta T_G}{\Delta P_G}$, and, by rearrangment of (5) and conversion to units of C_{IN} and Tm_G,

$$(9) \qquad \frac{\Sigma c_{in}}{C_{IN}} = 1 - \frac{\Delta T_G/Tm_G}{\Delta P_G C_{IN}/Tm_G}$$

or by rearrangement of (8)

$$(10) \qquad \frac{\Sigma tm}{Tm_G} = \frac{T_{G'}}{Tm_G} - P_{G'} \cdot C_{IN}/Tm_G \frac{\Delta T_G/Tm_G}{\Delta P_G C_{IN}/Tm_G}$$

where $T_{G'}$ and $P_{G'}$ are simultaneous values, and ΔT_G and ΔP_G are corresponding increments between $P_{G'}$ and $P_{G''}$.

By applying (9) and (10) at progressively higher values of P_G, the values of Σc_{in} and Σtm are calculated for an ever-increasingly large saturated portion of the kidney; the successive *increments* in these terms, which may be designated simply as c_{in} and tm, represent the absolute rates of filtration and the absolute quantity of tubular tissue in successive categories saturating at progressively higher values of P_G. Hence c_{in}/C_{IN} and tm/Tm expresses these terms as relative fractions of the total filtration rate or excretory capacity.

It is not only cumbersome to describe the glomerular activity, r, of various categories in absolute units (cc./mg./min.) but less illuminating than when this glomerular activity is expressed relative to r_{mean} for the kidneys as a whole. But r_{mean} is identical with $\Sigma c_{in}/\Sigma tm$, which in turn is identical with C_{IN}/Tm_G. Hence for any category which just saturates at $P_{G'}$, $P_{G'} c_{in} = tm$, and

$$(11) \qquad r/R = \frac{c_{in}/tm}{C_{IN}/Tm_G} = \frac{1}{P_{G'} C_{IN}/Tm_G}$$

The above ratio, r/R can be called the relative glomerular activity of a particular category.

In the work book the calculations are carried through from P_G, U_G and V, by means of (1), to the terms appearing in (9) and (10), the corresponding values of the titration curve being then plotted as in our Figures. Since $U_G V$ is determined from urine samples which of necessity are collected over relatively long periods of time, the titration curve[15] is broken into a relatively few linear seg-

---

[15] Any increase in P_G beyond the level required to saturate those nephrons having the highest glomerular activity can only be accompanied by either (a) saturation of nephrons having a lower glomerular activity, or (b) spilling of all filtered glucose in excess of the reabsorptive capacity of all available nephrons. In (a), $\Delta U_G V/\Delta P_G$ will necessarily increase as P_G is raised, approaching the maximal ratio of 1.0, which will obtain in (b). Since an increase in $\Delta U_G V/\Delta P_G$ requires a corresponding decrease in $\Delta T_G/\Delta P_G$ the titration curve relating T_G to P_G (or to $P_G C_{IN}/Tm_G$) will always be concave to the abscissae. That is, a kidney in which the dispersion of glomerular activity is constant throughout titration cannot yield a convex or sigmoid titration curve, and the presence of convexity implies a change in glomerular activity.

ments, the size of each segment being proportional to $\Delta U_G V$; i.e., in effect the kidneys are broken up into a small number of large categories. It has been our practice to collect 12 to 15 urine periods, and to draw a smooth titration curve through the resulting observations. Any point along this curve may be chosen arbitrarily as corresponding to the point of saturation of a category, the relative glomerular activity (r/R) of which is given by equation (11); it is then an equally arbitrary election whether the size of this category is to be expressed as a fraction of the total filtration rate (c_{in}/C_{IN}) or as a fraction of the total reabsorptive tissue (tm/Tm_G), but since Tm_G is presumably a constant in any one individual, the latter method of expression is preferable. Hence in practice only equation (10) is used in conjunction with (11).

2. The frequency distribution curve

A frequency distribution curve conventionally presents the number of individuals, or the per cent of the total population, in each of several "categories" of the "variable" under examination, where each category represents the same increment in this variable. If the dimensions of various categories were different, this circumstance would of course affect the relative number of individuals falling within them and the frequency distribution curve would lose its definitive meaning.

In the present problem the "variable" under examination is the relative glomerular activity, r/R, and it is required that the frequency distribution curve describe categories each of which represents the same increment ($\Delta r/R$) in this term. The minimal size of this increment could in principle be as small as the minimal difference between any two nephrons, but of course in practice experimental error precludes any such refinement and the minimal category size must be chosen arbitrarily. It must, moreover, be of the same size in all frequency distribution curves which are to be compared with each other. To this end we have chosen for the category dimension, $\Delta r/R$, the value 0.1, or 10 per cent of r_{mean}/R, the latter ratio of course having a value of 1.0 since these two terms are arithmetically identical.

Having determined from the titration curve the extreme lower (or upper) limit of r/R, values of r/R above (or below) the value are set down, each differing from its predecessor by 0.1; $P_G \cdot C_{IN}/Tm_G$ is then calculated as R/r, the corresponding value of T_G/Tm_G is read off from the smoothed titration curve, and tm/Tm_G is calculated by difference after the application of (10). Very slight differences in the slope of the titration curve result in marked differences in tm/Tm_G and consequently the resulting frequency distribution curve must be smoothed and interpreted with due consideration of this fact.

Since the frequency distribution curve for a particular subject, when expressed as above, shows only the distribution of glomerular activity relative to the subject's mean value, R, it fails to show whether R itself is above or below normal; for this purpose it is convenient to append a secondary scale, r/R_{normal}, so placed below r/R that there is coincidence between the zero ordinates of the two scales, and also between the ordinates $r/R = 1.0$ and R/R_{normal}, the values of R_{normal} for men and women being given in Table III. The two scales thus give at a glance both the relative and absolute glomerular activity throughout the kidneys. For illustration the reader is referred to Figure 9, etc.

3. Diodrast titration

The above principles are directly applicable to the determination of the relative perfusion rate of tubular tissue. Again the central fact is the circumstance that this tissue is characterized by a maximal capacity for the excretion of diodrast, which under premises A and B (page 78), and starting from equation (2) (page 62), may be translated into, terms of individual excretory units, or categories of such units.

The following symbols are used:

T_D = Total tubular excretion of diodrast iodine (mg. per min.).

Tm_D = Maximal value of T_D.

P_D = Plasma concentration of diodrast iodine (mg. per cc.).

C_{IN} = Glomerular filtration rate (cc. per min.).

$U_D V$ = Rate of excretion of diodrast iodine (mg. per min.).

F = Per cent free diodrast in plasma (see nomogram in reference 38).

W = Per cent protein-free water in plasma/100 (FW is taken as 0.73 in most calculations).

C_D = Plasma diodrast clearance or $U_D V/P_D$.

V_ϱ = Rate of perfusion of entire tubular excretory tissue.

E_p = Overall (arterial-venous) extraction ratio of diodrast.

$\bar{E}$ = Mean plasma extraction ratio of diodrast from plasma perfusing unsaturated tubular excretory tissue.

E = Plasma extraction ratio just at point of saturation.[16]

The next five terms are applicable in principle to a unit of tubular excretory tissue (tubule cell), or to an experimentally measured category of units having the same perfusion rate.

$\bar{v}_o$ = Rate of perfusion of unsaturated tubular excretory tissue.

v_o = Rate of perfusion of saturated tubular excretory tissue.

t = Rate of diodrast iodine excretion in unsaturated tubular excretory tissue (mg. per min.).

tm = Rate of diodrast iodine excretion in saturated tubular excretory tissue (mg. per min.).

r = Tubular perfusion rate (v_o/tm) in a particular unit of tubular excretory tissue.

tm/Tm_D = Size of a category having a particular perfusion rate, expressed as a fraction of the entire kidneys.

R = Tubular perfusion rate (V_o/Tm_D) of the entire kidneys.

R_{normal} = Average value of mean perfusion rate in normal subjects.

Two important differences between glucose and diodrast titration concern the determination of the volume of carrier.

---

[16] $\bar{E}$ and E are to be distinguished from E_p, the *overall* plasma extraction ratio, which is lower than either $\bar{E}$ or E in consequence of blood perfusing inert tissue.

First, during glucose titration, the total volume of carrier (glomerular filtrate) can be measured throughout the titration process. During diodrast titration, however, the elevation of the plasma diodrast concentration, by saturating some excretory units, lowers the overall extraction ratio of diodrast so that the excretion of this substance is no longer an index of renal plasma flow. Consequently the renal plasma flow must be measured at low plasma levels of diodrast prior to the elevation of the latter for titration purposes, and it must be assumed that this control figure will be applicable throughout the titration process—i.e., that the renal plasma flow will remain constant.

Second, during glucose titration, all the glomerular filtrate must be conceived as carrying glucose to the tubules. During diodrast titration, however, the effective volume of carrier must be equated with that nominal fraction of the plasma diodrast which is delivered to the parietal surface of the tubules— excluding the fraction which is filtered off by glomerular filtration—for only this fraction is available to be excreted by the tubular tissue or to participate in its saturation. The volume of plasma which is in effect diverted by filtration is FWC_{IN}, as in equation (2).[17] The volume of plasma which remains to perfuse the tubules may be calculated from the diodrast clearance, C_D, and the plasma extraction ratio, $\bar{E}$, of the tubular perfusate. The total rate of diodrast excretion, $U_D V$, is the sum of the diodrast excreted by filtration, or $P_D FWC_{IN}$, and that excreted by the tubules; at low values of P_D the latter term is equal to V_o, the volume of plasma perfusing the tubules, multiplied by $\bar{E}$, the extraction ratio across unsaturated tubules, and the plasma concentration, P_D:

$$(12) \qquad U_D V = P_D V_o \bar{E} + P_D FWC_{IN}$$

Dividing by P_D

$$(13) \qquad C_D = V_o \bar{E} + FWC_{IN}$$

Hence the volume of tubular perfusate is

$$(14) \qquad V_o = (C_D - FWC_{IN})/\bar{E}$$

and the load of diodrast carried to the tubules by this perfusate is

$$(15) \qquad P_D V_o = P_D (C_D - FWC_{IN})/\bar{E}$$

In equation (15) $\bar{E}$ is unknown, and not determinable even by means of simultaneous arterial and venous renal blood, for it refers specifically to blood perfusing active excretory tubular units, to the exclusion of blood perfusing inert

[17] It is immaterial whether the filtered diodrast is actually removed from plasma which subsequently passes to tubular tissue, or from plasma which never reaches tubular tissue; in the calculation of C_D all excreted diodrast is included, and whatever is excreted by filtration must be deducted in calculating tubular load. Insofar as the red cells carry diodrast, they will contribute to $U_D V$ and increase the apparent plasma clearance, but where the fraction of diodrast carried by the red cells remains constant at all plasma levels the resulting error will not influence the form of the titration curve. However, recent studies lead us to believe that red cell transport in man is negligible and the point may be neglected here.

tissue such as the fibrous and fatty capsule, connective tissue and non-excretory portions of the tubules. However, the overall extraction ratio, E_p, in the explanted kidney of the dog averages in the data of White (46) 0.75, and in those of Corcoran, Smith and Page (11), 0.85; since $\bar{E}$ refers only to the blood presented to active tubular tissue it is our belief that it is substantially above 0.90, and for our present purposes may be taken as 1.0. In which case V_o can be calculated from the other clinically measurable terms of (14).

In the diodrast titration it must be recognized that one tubule cell is presumably the anatomical unit of "saturation" (unlike glucose titration where an entire nephron must presumably be saturated before any of the filtered glucose delivered to that nephron will be excreted in the urine); and it must be assumed, as in premise A, that each cell will continue to excrete all diodrast delivered to it until saturation occurs—i.e., that there is no intrinsic splay in the cellular excretory mechanism.[18] This assumption is warranted by the narrow splay in the titration curve of the entire kidney, as shown in Figure 7.

Equations (16) to (24) which follow, are parallel to equations (3) to (11), except for the substitution of tubular excretion (T_D) for tubular reabsorption (T_G).

Let the plasma diodrast concentration, P_D, be raised to a level $P_{D'}$, at which an appreciable quantity of tubular tissue is just saturated; then

$$(16) \qquad EP_{D'}\Sigma v_o = \Sigma tm$$

where Σv_o is the total rate of perfusion of the saturated tissue, and Σtm is the total quantity of tubular tissue in the saturated portion, while E is the extraction ratio of diodrast in the perfusion v_o at $P_{D'}$.[19] Here Σv_o is conceived as expressing the virtual flow per minute of a fluid having the same concentration of diodrast as the post glomerular plasma.

[18] This is not true, apparently, of phenol red, but it does appear to be true of diodrast since the normal titration curve, as shown in Figure 7, is a relatively sharp angle. If saturation did not occur until the excretory tissue were presented with an excess load, this circumstance would give the appearance of a splay in the titration curve. Were such a splay present, the question would have to be answered whether it is attributable to lack of uniformity in perfusion rate, or to an inherent characteristic of tubular kinetics; but since an appreciable splay is normally absent, the question has little importance for the normal kidney. Where splay does appear, as in J. G. and E. F. (fig. 8) it must be a result of a disproportion in either the numerator or denominator of the ratio, v_o/tm; if attributed to the latter, it might be attributed to a change in the intrinsic behavior of each excretory unit, but the argument has little importance when one is dealing not only with two million odd nephrons, but with many times this number of excretory cells; i.e., the units of excretion are so small and so numerous that for nearly all purposes we may consider them as quantitatively fixed in excretory capacity. Partial loss of capacity in individual cells in consequence of some pathological process would be equivalent, so far as the titration method is concerned, to a reduction in cell size, and we cannot apriori suppose that all cells normally have exactly the same excretory capacity.

[19] We have elsewhere (35) pointed out that diodrast molecules not available for clearance at low plasma concentrations (C_D) will not in all probability be made available for tubular saturation (Tm_D) merely in consequence of increasing the plasma diodrast concentration. Hence E may be taken as equal $\bar{E}$, which we take equal to 1.0.

Now let $P_{D'}$ be raised to $P_{D''}$, a level sufficiently high to cause the tubular tissue in the unsaturated portion to excrete a measurably increased quantity of diodrast, but not high enough to saturate any additional tissue. For all unsaturated tissue (writing $P_{D''} - P_{D'} = \Delta P_D$),

$$(17) \qquad\qquad \Sigma \bar{v}_0 = \frac{\Delta T_D}{\Delta P_D \bar{E}}$$

where $\Sigma \bar{v}_0$ is the total perfusion rate of the unsaturated tissue, ΔT_D is the increment in total tubular excretion and $\bar{E}$ is the extraction ratio of the diodrast in the perfusate going to this unsaturated tissue.

The total volume of plasma, V_o, perfusing all tubular tissue is equal to the sum of that perfusing the saturated portion, $\Sigma \underline{v}_o$, and that perfusing the unsaturated portion, $\Sigma \bar{v}_o$:

$$(18) \qquad\qquad V_o = \Sigma \underline{v}_o + \Sigma \bar{v}_o$$

The total tubular excretion of diodrast is equal to the sum of diodrast excreted by the saturated portion, Σtm, and the unsaturated portion, Σt:

$$(19) \qquad\qquad T_D = \Sigma tm + \Sigma t$$

The rate of excretion by the unsaturated portion is

$$(20) \qquad\qquad \Sigma t = P_{D'} \Sigma \bar{v}_o \bar{E}$$

From (17), (19) and (20),

$$(21) \qquad\qquad \Sigma tm = T_D - P_{D'} \frac{\Delta T_D}{\Delta P_D}$$

where T_D and P_D are simultaneous values, and $P_{D'}$ is the lower value of ΔP_D. $\bar{E}$ has cancelled out since both (17) and (20) refer to the same unsaturated nephrons.

To collate different individuals in terms of T_D/Tm_D and $P_D V_o/Tm$, we may substitute (17) in (18) and convert to units of V_o and Tm_D :

$$(22) \qquad\qquad \frac{\Sigma v_0}{V_0} = 1 - \frac{\Delta T_D/Tm_D}{\bar{E}\Delta P_D\, V_0/Tm_D}$$

Introducing the same units into (21):

$$(23) \qquad\qquad \frac{tm}{Tm_D} = \frac{T_{D'}}{Tm_D} - \frac{P_{D'}\, V_0 \Delta T_D/Tm_D}{Tm_D \Delta P_D\, V_0/Tm_D}$$

Since in any category which just saturates at $P_{D'}$, $EP_{D'}\, v_0 = tm$, it follows that $r = 1/EP_{D'}$. Dividing both sides by V_0/Tm_D

$$(24) \qquad\qquad \frac{r}{R} = \frac{v_0/tm}{V_0/Tm_D} = \frac{1}{EP_{D'}\, V_0/Tm_D}$$

Here $V_o = (C_D - FWC_{IN})/\bar{E}$ (equation 14), and substitution leads to the term $E/\bar{E}$, where E is the diodrast extraction ratio in the plasma perfusing a particular category just at saturation, and $\bar{E}$ the extraction ratio of diodrast from the entire tubular perfusate at low plasma levels (whence V_o is determined). Since $\bar{E}$ is certainly above 0.90 and probably close to 1.0 (see footnote 19), the ratio $E/\bar{E}$ may for practical purposes be taken as unity, whence

$$(25) \qquad \frac{r}{R} = \frac{1}{P_{D'}(C_D - FWC_{IN})/Tm_D}$$

where all the terms are clinically determinable. In all calculations here V_o is taken as equal to $C_D - FWC_{IN}$. Equation (25) yields the relative tubular perfusion, or the tubular perfusion of a category expressed relative to the mean tubular perfusion of the entire kidneys as unity.

In the working equations (22), (23) and (25), the definitive value of Tm_D is presumed to have been determined independently of the titration process. Since Tm_D rather than V_o is the fixed physiological term, tm/Tm_D (equation 23) rather than v_o/V_o (equation 22) has been chosen to designate units of renal tissue the perfusion rate of which is under examination, and the values of tm/Tm_D are calculated as the differences between the successive values of $\Sigma tm/Tm_D$ obtained by application of (equation 23) to progressively higher values of T_D interpolated in the smoothed titration curve at selected values of P_D. The latter are selected at intervals of $r/R = 0.1$, beginning at either end of the titration curve, for the reasons stated in the discussion of glomerular activity.

4. Theoretical implications of the titration methods

In order to visualize the application of the titration methods, we have presented in Figure 5 three symmetrical frequency distribution curves applicable to either c_{in}/tm or v_o/tm, and the corresponding titration curves.[20] For a discussion of the statistical characteristics of these curves the reader is referred to the accompanying legend.

In considering the limits of dispersion in glomerular activity and tubular perfusion which might, on a statistical basis alone, be expected in the normal kidney, it may be noted that the standard deviation (σ) among various physiological variables usually ranges from 14 to 20 per cent of the mean. It will be recalled that the standard deviation expressed in per cent of the mean ($100\sigma/m$) is called the coefficient of variation. An interesting list of coefficients of variation for various physiological variables is given by Pearl (25); $100\sigma/m$ is less than 14 per cent chiefly in anatomically rigid characters, such as body and bone measurements, while it is greater than 20 per cent in clinically unselected or

[20] In calculating the titration curve corresponding to a given frequency distribution curve, the range of r/R must be fitted to the configuration of the curve in such a manner that the mean value of v_o/tm divided by the mean value of r/R shall equal V_o/Tm; that is, the condition must be fulfilled that for the category which stands at the center of gravity of the curve, $v_o/tm = V_o/Tm$. This is most easily accomplished by a process of approximation, starting by setting $r/R = 1.0$ opposite $\Sigma tm/Tm = 0.5$, and raising or lowering r/R if Σv_o is less or greater than 1.0, until $\Sigma v_o = 1.0$, when $\Sigma tm/Tm = 1.0$. In this reverse calculation, $r/R \times tm/Tm = v_o/V_o$; if Tm is taken as equal to 1.0, $T = \Sigma tm + P(1 - \Sigma v_o/V_o)$. where $P = R/r$.

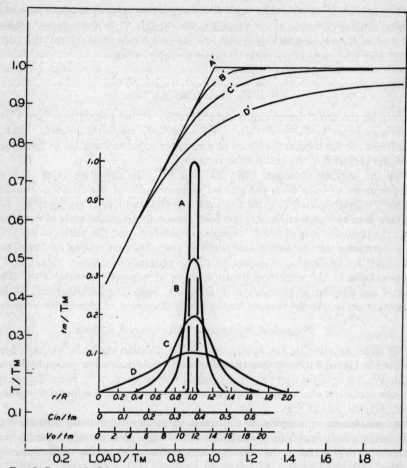

Fig. 5. Symmetrical frequency distribution curves and corresponding titration curves. The curves are equally applicable to the distribution of glomerular activity or tubular perfusion, and are discussed as though r/R may be read in either sense. The curves are constructed to illustrate the following conditions:

A. *Where r/R is identical for all nephrons.* Here all nephrons will saturate at a load/Tm ratio = 1.0, and the titration curve will follow the abrupt angle, A'.

B. *Where r/R is distributed in conformity with the "normal" frequency distribution curve, the dispersion being such that 95.4 per cent of the nephrons fall within the range of 0.80 to 1.20 times the mean.* The titration curve, B', departs from the sharp angle A' so little that the deviation is practically undetectable.

C. *A "normal" frequency distribution, with the dispersion such that only 68.3 per cent of the nephrons fall within the range of 0.80 to 1.20 times the mean, 95.4 per cent falling within the range of 0.60 to 1.40 times the mean.* The titration curve, C', deviates from A' to an extent which is, from the technical point of view, generally determinable in the case of c_{in}/tm, and determinable under favorable conditions in the case of v_o/tm.

With this degree of dispersion σ has a value of 20 per cent of the mean, and in the text reasons have been given for presuming that this degree of dispersion is of the order to be expected in physiological variables such as glomerular activity and tubular perfusion.

D. *The dispersion of r/R is maximally increased.* Since r/R must approach zero as a lower limit, symmetry requires that the upper limit approach 2.0. The titration curve, D',

definitely pathological organ weights where extreme variations are to be anticipated, or in psychodependent characters such as rapidity and steadiness of hand, visual acuity and dermal sensitivity. It lies between 15 and 20 per cent in most counterbalanced or regulated physiological functions, such as pulse rate, respiratory rate, vital capacity, reaction time, auditory acuity, normal liver, heart and kidney weights, and the like. It may also be noted that in different subjects various features of renal function have values for $100\sigma/m$ ranging from 13 to 20 per cent, as shown in Table III. It cannot of course be argued that the dispersion of a variable in different subjects bears directly on the dispersion of the same variable between nephrons in any one subject, yet where two counterbalanced functions are involved, as in c_{in}/tm and v_o/tm, we may reasonably anticipate the same order of magnitude of dispersion.

In curve C of Figure 5, $100\sigma/m$ is assigned a value of 20 per cent; since the curve is given a "normal" frequency distribution, it follows that 68.3 per cent of

---

begins to splay when $load/Tm = 0.5$ (which in relation to saturation corresponds to $r/R = 2.0$) and rises towards Tm as an asymptote which is reached only when $load/Tm = \infty$ (corresponding to $r/R = 0.0$).

Deformation resulting from independent variation. The so-called "normal" frequency distribution curves shown above are derived by aid of probability theory, the curve being calculated by means of the binomial equation $(p + q)^n$, where $p + q = 1$, and $p = q$ (i.e., $p = 0.5$ and $q = 0.5$). Where deformation of this curve is attributable to circumstances which may act on the value of r/R in one nephron independently of any other nephron— i.e., where variation of any one nephron (p) is independent of variation in any other (q)— the resulting skewed curve will still be described by the equation $(p + q)^n$ where $p + q = 1$, but q will no longer be equal to p. Setting q at very small values and taking n at appropriately large values leads to unimodal curves resembling v_o/tm in Figures 8 and 10. Moderate deformation by 'independent variation' leads to curves so slightly skewed that in the titration curve the observations remain close within the angle, A', and are not distinguishable in practice from such a curve as B'. Deformation by 'independent variation' appears to be characteristic of tubular perfusion in the cases of essential hypertension studied here.

Deformation arising otherwise than by independent variation. Where variation in one nephron is not independent of variation in others, but where certain nephrons are affected *because* others are affected or where large numbers are necessarily affected simultaneously, and where the circumstances giving rise to variation are unknown, the course of deformation of the distribution curve cannot be predicted. In principle, the frequency distribution curve could take an infinite variety of shapes. Two general trends might, however, be expected: a shift in population towards low (or high) categories could occur in such a manner as to produce a unimodal curve skewed to right or left, in the general manner of 'independent variation' curves where $p > q$ (resembling v_o/tm, fig. 10); or the population may become divided into two or more groups—one severely affected and the other unaffected—leading to the production of distribution curves with two or more modes (such as c_{in}/tm in figs. 10, 11, etc.). Deformation indicative of variation of the latter type is particularly evident in glomerular activity distribution curves in our subjects with essential hypertension.

Reference to mean normal values. The reader will note that since the ratio, r/R, has been taken as the essential physiological variable in defining our frequency distribution curve, all such curves for different individuals are strictly comparable, both in respect to total area and to the mean, or center of gravity (where $r/R = 1.0$). The advantages of this method of presentation are obvious, but these advantages are in some measure offset by the consequence that the absolute values of r (i.e., of c_{in}/tm and v_o/tm) are lost by reference to the mean (R), and hence there is available no information on whether the mean is above or below the normal mean. It is therefore convenient to append a second scale in which r/R_{normal} is set in apposition to $r/R = 1.0$. This has been done in all subsequent Figures, but in the present Figure this would amount to mere duplication since $R = R_{normal}$; consequently the secondary scale has here been made to read in *absolute units* by setting in apposition to $r/R = 1.0$ the absolute mean normal values for men $(C_{IN}/Tm_G = 0.371$ and $V_o/Tm_D = 11.6)$. For women, $C_{IN}/Tm_G = 0.395$ and $V_o/Tm_D = 11.9$. The values for C_{IN}/Tm_G are taken from Table III (combined series). V_o/Tm_D is calculated as $(C_D - 0.73\,C_{IN})/Tm_D$, using the respective male and female mean normal values for these terms as given in the above Table.

the observations will fall within the range of $m \pm \sigma$. Assuming that c_{in}/tm or v_o/tm is symmetrically distributed in accordance with the normal frequency distribution, curve C would then represent the anticipated distribution curve, and C' the corresponding titration curve, for either glomerular activity or tubular perfusion.

5. Sources of error and permissible corrections

It is frequently difficult to obtain complete emptying of the bladder, even with 20 cc. of washout fluid, and this source of error, coupled with errors in timing the end of successive collection periods, may lead to a rough, alternate staggering in the titration curve. Where such errors are present they are generally revealed by the alternation of low and high values for the filtration rate, and it seems permissible to correct for them by correcting the urine volume in such a manner as to yield for the two successive periods a constant filtration rate equal to the mean value of the two periods. The correction, however, should not be extended beyond two successive periods unless it is evident that the filtration rate has remained constant for a longer period of time.

Wherever P_G or P_D are changing significantly, two and a half minutes should be deducted for "delay time" elapsed between the sampling of blood and the appearance in the bladder of urine formed from this blood (8, 37).

Since the titration curve is a smoothed curve, and the frequency distribution curve is further smoothed between the calculated values of tm/TmG or tm/Tm_D, the latter is not to be given more weight than is warranted by the overall contours of either.

The discovery of glomeruli of relatively low activity is practically difficult since it depends upon minute changes in U_GV at a time when P_G is relatively large, and when small errors in P_G or in C_{IN} produce large errors in the calculation of T_G. But the discovery of glomeruli of relatively high activity is comparatively simple, since they will saturate at relatively low values of P_G and hence their presence will be revealed by the appearance of glucose in the urine at P_GC_{IN}/Tm_G ratios lower than 1.0. The normal excretion of total reducing substances, which ranges from 0.5 to 2.0 mg. per minute, is quite constant in any one subject in successive clearance periods and serves as a satisfactory base line from which to detect increased glucose excretion. An increment in U_GV of 2.5 mg. per minute above the basal excretion of total reducing substances is well within practical determination. This represents less than one per cent of the total reabsorptive capacity of the kidney, and by appropriate adjustment of P_G, saturation of this fraction of tubular tissue is in principle detectable.

Tm_G must frequently be estimated at P_GC_{IN}/T_G ratios less than 2.0, and where there are significant numbers of nephrons having a relative glomerular activity less than 0.5, this fact may lead to an error in Tm_G measurement. If Tm_G is taken at too small a value, this error tends to decrease the splay in the titration curve and to deform the distribution curve by narrowing the limits of dispersion. In the net, however, a titration curve is obtained which describes the distribution of glomerular activity in those glomeruli the tubules of which are accessible to glucose saturation, and this distribution will probably not differ greatly in most instances from the distribution with all nephrons taken into account.

It has been noted that in diodrast titration the volume of carrier to the tubules, V_o, must be determined independently of the titration process, and preferably just before titration is begun. It is then assumed that the renal plasma flow remains constant during titration. We believe that with the proper precautions this condition will generally be fulfilled, but it is obviously the major weakness of the diodrast titration method. Exceptions are noted in the discussion of individual subjects in the following section.

The discovery of tubules of relatively high perfusion rate is rendered the more difficult by possible changes in total tubular perfusion, a decrease in the latter giving the effect of a depression of T_D in consequence of tubular saturation; hence the titration should be carried out under conditions favoring a stable renal blood flow. In curve D, for example, saturation of the first tubular tissue would occur at $P_D V_o / Tm_D = 0.5$, but since V_o / Tm_D rarely exceeds 20, this would require a value of $P_D = 0.05$ mgm. per cc.; i.e., the diodrast clearance would not be depressed at values of P_D (1.0 to 3.0 mg. per cent) ordinarily used in this measurement. The last tubular tissue to saturate, having a perfusion rate approaching zero, would not saturate except at very high values of P_D; but Tm_D can readily be determined at high values of P_D, where the load/Tm_D ratio = 3.0 or more, and hence the errors in Tm_D measurement can be reduced to negligible proportions.

VI. DISTRIBUTION OF GLOMERULAR ACTIVITY AND TUBULAR PERFUSION IN THE NORMAL KIDNEY

Figures 6 and 7 present data on the titration of normal subjects with glucose and diodrast. Important details relative to both groups of data are discussed in the legends.

In some subjects glomerular activity is so nearly uniform throughout the kidneys that no splay can be detected in the titration curve, i.e., this curve closely follows the angle A' of Figure 5. Most subjects, however, show a slight splay, but this is so little that, in view of the practical difficulties in controlling P_G at precisely the proper level, it is difficult to get more than one or two samples of urine in the critical angle. For this reason no attempt has been made to present or analyze separately the titration curves of different individuals, all data being given in a mass diagram and averaged into a single titration curve (insert in Figure 6). Taking this curve as representing the average variations in glomerular activity, it may be said that in no appreciable number[21] of nephrons is glomerular activity below 0.60 or above 1.5 times the mean glomerular activity for the entire kidneys, and that the activity is distributed about the mean

---

[21] In view of the practical difficulties of slowly raising P_G over the critical range, and of the accurate collection of closely spaced urine samples, the above data do not represent the most rigorous application of the titration method, and in evaluating our present data we would not restrict the word "appreciable" to less than 5 per cent of the total tubular tissue.

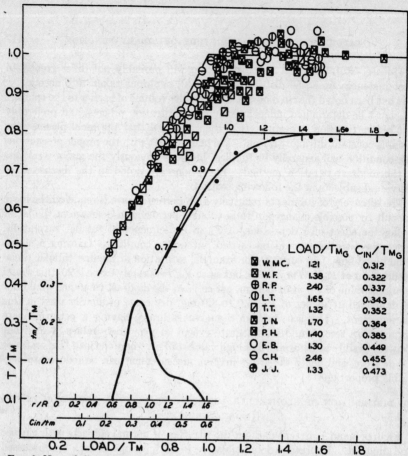

LOAD/T_{MG} | C_{IN}/T_{MG}

	LOAD/T_{MG}	C_{IN}/T_{MG}
W. MC.	1.21	0.312
W. F.	1.38	0.322
R. P.	2.40	0.337
L. T.	1.65	0.343
T. T.	1.32	0.352
I. N.	1.70	0.364
P. H.	1.40	0.385
E. B.	1.30	0.449
C. H.	2.46	0.455
J. J.	1.33	0.473

FIG. 6. Normal dispersion of glomerular activity. Mass plot of glucose titrations on ten normal subjects, some of whom were titrated on two or more occasions. The mass plot shows more scatter than is present in any one individual, but since one individual may be expected to vary slightly on different occasions, the mass plot may be taken as roughly representative of the normal variation.

For the calculation of the frequency distribution curve, the observations, of which there are 150, were averaged in blocks of Δ load/Tm = 0.1. These averaged observations are shown in the inset, the smooth titration curve being drawn by visual approximation. The limits of relative glomerular activity are set at 0.60 and 1.50, since glucose excretion does not normally begin below a load/T_G ratio of 0.60 and, from the data presented in Tables I and II, we believe that Tm_G is reached at a load/T_G ratio of 1.5.

The frequency distribution curve as drawn would indicate that in a small proportion of nephrons relative glomerular activity (r/R) is greater than would be expected on chance distribution alone, with the consequence that the mode is shifted to slightly below the mean. It must be emphasized, however, that the use of data from different individuals, combined with the narrow limits of dispersion, caution against attaching significance to minor changes in the frequency distribution curve, which is extremely sensitive to changes in the angle of the titration curve. The above frequency distribution curve must be considered as practically identical with the symmetrical normal frequency distribution curve C shown in Figure 5. So interpreted, it may be said that *glomerular activity in the normal kidney is distributed about the mean in a manner roughly conforming with a normal frequency distribution curve, the dispersion of which is such that 95 per cent of the observations fall within ±40 per cent of the mean.* (However, in some individuals, such as J. J., E. B., C. H., L. T., W. Mc., whose titration curves are sharply angular, the dispersion is so narrow that the glucose titration method is technically inadequate for a definitive examination. Subjects T. T. and I. N. pull the average titration curve out from the angle and are responsible for the skewing of the distribution curve to the right.)

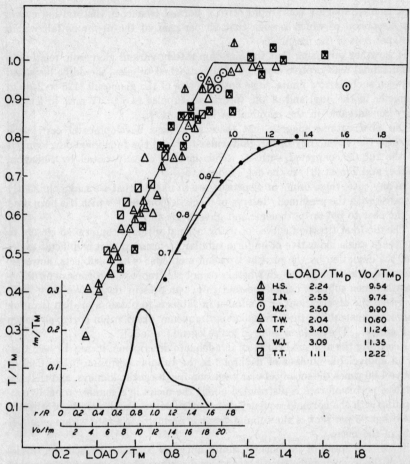

FIG. 7. Normal dispersion of tubular perfusion.   Mass plot of diodrast titrations of seven normal subjects, some of whom were titrated twice.   The mass plot contains 70 observations which were averaged by blocks of Δ load/$Tm = 0.1$.   The averaged data are shown in the inset, the smooth titration curve being drawn by visual approximation.   The limits of relative tubular perfusion are conformably placed at 0.66 and 1.66.   The lower figure cannot be set with accuracy, chiefly because of the error inherent in assuming a constant value for V_o, a difficulty discussed in the description of the diodrast titration method.   The upper limit is taken as an extrapolation of the smooth titration curve, and is probably maximal. It must be recognized, however, that the uncertainty attached to the limits of the titration curve, and hence of the distribution curve, involves only a small percentage of the total tubular tissue.

As in the case of Figure 6, the frequency distribution curve is practically identical with the normal frequency distribution curve C in Figure 5.   The same qualifications must be applied to the massing of data obtained from different individuals as in the case of glucose titration.   Accepting the curve as drawn, it may be said that *relative tubular perfusion in the normal kidney is distributed about the mean in a manner roughly conforming with a normal frequency distribution curve, the dispersion of which is such that 95 per cent of the observations fall within ±40 per cent of the mean.*   (Again it must be noted that in some individuals such as H. S. and T. F., whose titration curve is sharply angular, the dispersion is very narrow, while a few periods only on I. N. are responsible for much of the skew to the right.)

in a manner roughly conforming with a normal frequency distribution curve, the dispersion of which is such that 95 per cent of the nephrons fall within ±40 per cent of the mean.

It is rather surprising that the filtration rate in various glomeruli, relative to the maximal reabsorptive capacity of the attached tubules, should be dispersed between such narrow limits, since both the size of the glomeruli (125 to 246μ in diameter in the dog) and of the (proximal) tubules (4.8 to 17 mm. in length) vary considerably in the mammalian kidney.

Our observations suggest that there is a close developmental correlation between the vascularity of the glomerular tuft and the functional development of the tubule connected with it, a relationship already noted by Shannon, Farber and Troast (31) in the dog's kidney.

In any case, these limits of dispersion are so narrow that we may confidently dispense with the presumed "reserve of inactive glomeruli" which has been used in the past to bolster pathologic and physiologic theory.

The diodrast titration curves of many normal subjects conform so closely to the sharp angle indicative of uniform tubular perfusion that it is difficult to detect the deviation by the present titration methods. Other subjects, however, show a definite splay, though whether or not this represents a consistent difference between subjects cannot be said from our present data. We have again averaged the observations on a number of subjects to obtain a median titration curve, and calculated the corresponding frequency distribution curve, as shown in Figure 7. The reader is referred to the legend for details.

Accepting the averaged curve as an adequate description, it may be said that in no appreciable number of nephrons is the tubular perfusion below 0.66 or above 1.66 times the mean tubular perfusion for the entire kidneys, and that the relative perfusion rate is distributed about the mean in a manner roughly conforming with the normal frequency distribution curve, the dispersion of which is such that 95 per cent of the tubular tissue is perfused at a rate within ±40 per cent of the mean.

If we may speak of the normal "uniformity" of perfusion without contradiction of the frequency distribution curve as described above, we would note that this uniformity has an entirely different physiologic basis than the (statistically) comparable uniformity of glomerular activity throughout the kidneys. Until contrary evidence is available, we lean to the presumption that diodrast excretion is exclusively a function of the proximal segment, which is for the most part restricted to the renal cortex. In this view, the diodrast titration method reveals the perfusion rate chiefly of the cortical tubules. These, as indeed all other tubules, are in fact perfused not directly by blood but by interstitial fluid; each minute some 130 cc. of water are reabsorbed by the tubules to traverse the interstitial space and to return to the capillary bed;[22] and in view of the convolutions of the cortical tubules, as opposed to the more rectilinear arrangement of the capillaries, there is probably a considerable and perhaps very devious circu-

[22] It is estimated that some 80 per cent of this fluid is reabsorbed in the proximal tubule (41).

lation of this interstitial fluid which would operate to maintain uniformity of tubular perfusion even in areas where moderate to severe arteriolar lesions are present.   Lastly, it should not be overlooked that tubular perfusion, as examined by the titration method, concerns individual tubule cells rather than entire nephrons, as in the case of glucose, and consequently physical diffusion of diodrast may contribute to the observed uniformity of perfusion.   If such is the case, oxygen and other plasma solutes of higher diffusion velocity must be distributed even more effectively.

The above considerations relative to the physiological basis of the normal uniformity of glomerular activity and tubular perfusion, are obviously important in interpreting the course of renal disease.

VII. DISTRIBUTION OF GLOMERULAR ACTIVITY AND TUBULAR PERFUSION IN THE HYPERTENSIVE KIDNEY

Figures 8 to 13 present data on the titration with glucose and diodrast of seven hypertensive subjects.   In examining the diseased kidney, it is necessary to consider each subject separately, since no two subjects can be expected to show comparable patterns in the renal circulation, and the reader is therefore referred to the accompanying legends for details of application and interpretations.   We will note here only certain general features of the renal circulation in the diseased kidney.

Except for the two subjects who have only one kidney (fig. 8) no large block of ischemic parenchyma is observed.   In three subjects (S. K., S. W. and Y. F.) the limits of dispersion in perfusion rate do not significantly exceed the normal; in three (E. F., A. M. and S. D.) the lower limit lies between 40 and 50 per cent of the mean normal value, while in only one (B. S.) it lies at about 30 per cent of the mean normal value.[23]

In sharp contrast to this tendency towards persistence of normal tubular perfusion, is a tendency towards abnormal glomerular activity.   Out of seven subjects in whom glucose titration was successfully completed (five being shown here), five subjects (T. T., A. C., S. K., S. W. and B. S.) show as lower limits of relative glomerular activity 25 to 40 per cent of the mean normal value (to be compared with a lower limit of 60 per cent in normal subjects).   This preponderance, even in a small series, of low glomerular activity implies the existence of arteriolar obstructive lesions.

Moreover, five out of seven subjects (T. T., A. C., S. K., S. W. and A. M.) show a definitely bimodal frequency distribution curve, notably illustrated by S. K.   Such a bimodal curve implies that in large numbers of glomeruli the filtration rate has been reduced simultaneously, an effect to be anticipated if obstructive lesions were to occur in the larger arteries, in such positions that obstruction of one artery would reduce the filtration pressure in numerous de-

[23] It would be untimely to argue the physiologic significance of this or that degree of focal ischemia in the causation or course of the hypertensive process, especially since these patients were examined after bed rest and in an essentially basal condition, and we shall confine this discussion to an exposition of the methods as such.

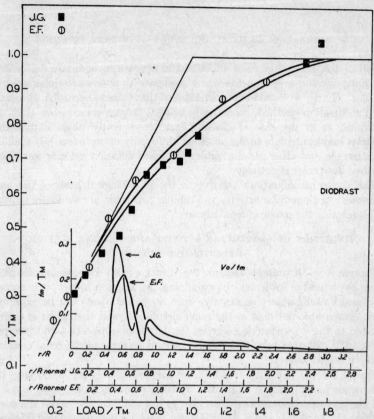

Fig. 8. E. F., 48 year old white female. Hypertension of many years duration, falling to moderate levels on bed rest. B.P. ranged from 230/130 to 160/86 mm. Hg. Heart enlarged; ECG showed left deviation; no evidence of congestive failure. Patient entered the hospital because of cerebral vascular accident. Retinae showed moderate vascular sclerosis, with normal discs and no hemorrhages or areas of degeneration. Urine was positive for protein, negative for blood. Concentrating capacity normal. Intravenous pyelograms showed no concentration of diodrast in the right renal pelvis; the left visualized normally. Right kidney removed on 1/26/42: diagnosis, atrophic pyelonephritic kidney. Diagnosis: essential hypertension; hypertensive and arteriosclerotic heart disease; cerebral vascular accident; atrophic pyelonephritis. On 2/12/40, $C_D = 354$, $C_{IN} = 83$, $Tm_D = 37.2$ (load/$T_D = 2.0$), B.P. = 163/109. On 2/16/40 (titration) $C_D = 416$, $C_{IN} = 89$, B.P. = 150/80, $V_o/Tm = 9.44$ (79 per cent of normal). The titration curve is technically good, with no infusion hyperemia.

J. G., 45 year old white female. Hypertension of relatively short duration. B.P. ranged from 200/120 to 150/80 mm. Hg, falling promptly on bed rest. Heart not enlarged; ECG showed left deviation; no evidence of congestive failure. Retinae showed mild vascular sclerosis, with normal discs and no hemorrhage or areas of degeneration. Urine was negative for protein and blood. Concentrating capacity normal. Some years previous to these observations the right kidney had been removed for tuberculosis. There was no evidence of tuberculosis in the remaining kidney. Diagnosis: essential hypertension. On 1/9/42, $C_D = 413$, $Tm_D = 40.7$ (load/$T_D = 3.4$). On the day of titration (1/16/42), $C_D = 463$, which figure is used in the calculation. The titration curve is technically good, but T fell in periods 13, 14 and 15, concurrently with a marked fall in C_M. $V_o/Tm = 10.1$ (85 per cent of normal).

In both of these subjects there has presumably been some compensatory hypertrophy of the tubules of the remaining kidney, since Tm_D is considerably larger than one-half the mean normal value. Local disproportion in the hypertrophy of tubules and vascular channels may explain the increased dispersion of tubular perfusion, some tissue being extremely hyperemic, while a substantial fraction is quite ischemic. (The secondary modes in the distribution curves are attributable to the circumstance that, as drawn, the titration curves are nearly linear between load/T_D ratios of 0.9 and 1.4.)

122

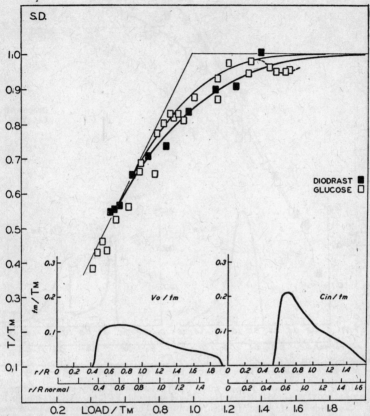

Fig. 9. S. D., 60 year old white female. Hypertension of many years duration. Blood pressure ranged from 224/130 to 186/118 mm. Hg. Heart enlarged; ECG showed left deviation of the electrical axis with inversion of the T waves in leads 1 and 2. No evidence of congestive heart failure. Retinae showed advanced vascular disease; discs normal; no hemorrhages or areas of degeneration. Urine negative for protein and blood; concentrating capacity normal. No history suggesting glomerulonephritis, pyelonephritis or uropathology. Intravenous pyelogram normal.

Died at age of 61 of cerebral hemorrhage. Diagnosis: essential hypertension with hypertensive and arteriosclerotic heart disease and cerebral arteriosclerosis. The patient had widespread arteriolar and arteriosclerosis. On 12/19/41, $C_M = 51$, $C_D = 216$, $Tm_D = 14.8$ (load$/T_D$ ratio = 7.7), B.P. = 212/120. On 12/23/41 with diodrast titration, $C_M = 43.3$, $C_D = 217$, $Tm_D = 16.8$ (load$/T_D$ ratio = 2.3), B.P. = 210/114. On 1/21/42 with diodrast titration repeated, $C_M = 38.1$, $C_D = 219$, B.P. = 216/116. On 1/26/42 with glucose titration, $C_M = 46.1$, C_D steady during titration at 185 to 222. $Tm_G = 129$ (load$/T_G = 1.1$). B.P. = 216/114. $V_o/Tm_D = 10.1$, or 85 per cent of normal. $C_{IN}/Tm_G = 0.358$, or 91 per cent of normal.

This patient shows no decrease in mean tubular perfusion (100 per cent of normal) and only a slight decrease in glomerular activity (91 per cent of normal), while the frequency distribution curves relative to both functions deviate only slightly from the normal. There is a small quantity of tubular tissue which is perfused at a subnormal rate ($r/R_{normal} = 0.4–0.6$) which is balanced by some hyperemic tissue having a perfusion rate as high as 80 per cent above normal. (The reader should compare this curve for v_o/tm with the normal curve in Fig. 7.) But this degree of deviation from normal is scarcely remarkable. Similarly, the distribution of glomerular filtrate is so nearly normal as to invite no comment, beyond the emphasis that in a 60 year old woman with hypertension of many years duration, and within one year of death, in whom the total filtration rate has been reduced to 40 per cent of normal, Tm_D to 37 per cent of normal, and Tm_G to 42 per cent of normal, the circulatory status of residual functional units is practically normal in pattern.

123

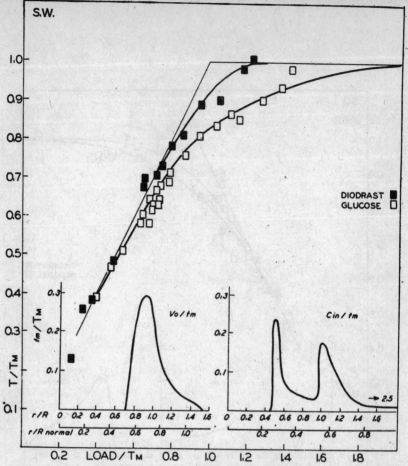

FIG. 10. S. W., 61 year old white male. Hypertension of many years duration. B.P. ranged from 220/128 to 190/110 mm. Hg. Heart enlarged; ECG showed left bundle branch block. No evidence of congestive heart failure. The retinae showed marked vascular sclerosis, with no hemorrhages or areas of degeneration and normal discs. Urine negative for protein and blood. Concentrating capacity normal. Clinical diagnosis: essential hypertension and hypertensive and arteriosclerotic heart disease. No previous history suggesting glomerulonephritis, pyelonephritis or uropathology. The clinical findings are indicative of widespread arteriolar and arteriosclerosis. On 11/21/40, $C_D = 375$, $C_{IN} = 74$, with partial diodrast and glucose titration, B.P. = 230/135. On 11/29/40, $C_D = 366$, $C_{IN} = 71$, followed by diodrast titration and partial glucose titration, B.P. = 200/110. On 12/6/40, $Tm_D = 36.5$ (load/T_D ratio = 3.1 to 4.22), B.P. = 194/112. On 12/11/40, $C_D = 420$, increasing to 594 during glucose titration, B.P. = 190/105. $V_o/Tm = 8.63$, or 74 per cent of normal. Glucose Tm (= 344) was determined on 12/11/40 at load/T_G = 1.38 to 1.49. Partial titrations on 11/21/40, 11/29/40 and 12/11/40. $C_{IN}/Tm_G = 0.206$, or 55 per cent of normal.

The total tubular perfusion of this subject is only 78 per cent of normal, but the distribution of perfusate is essentially normal.

The mean glomerular activity is only 55 per cent of normal and C_{IN}, which in 18 periods averages 71, is at the level of -2.7σ relative to the normal mean. Since Tm_G is close to, though not above the mean normal value, it is inferred that this low glomerular activity reflects moderately severe impairment of the filtration bed. It will be noted that the subject is one of the few who falls so aberrantly in Figure 4 as to suggest some unusual feature in the glomerular or vascular bed. It is to be noted, however, that the mean tubular perfusion, which is distributed in an essentially normal manner, is reduced much less than is the mean glomerular activity.

The glucose titration curve is extrapolated in its upper portion; more uniform flexion would tend to lower the left-hand peak of the distribution curve and fill the intervening trough. As drawn, it indicates that the reduction in filtration rate is extreme in approximately 30 per cent of the glomeruli, but no tolerable change in the titration curve would entirely abolish bimodality, or the indication that some large proportion of glomeruli have an extremely low activity.

It is noteworthy that an essentially uniform perfusion of the tubules can be maintained in spite of vascular lesions so severe as to impair glomerular activity to this extent.

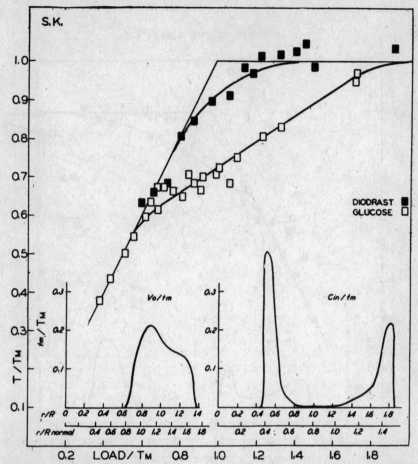

FIG. 11. S. K., 46 year old white male. Hypertension of relatively short duration. Blood pressure ranged from 210/134 to 140/100 mm. Hg. Heart enlarged; ECG showed left deviation of the electrical axis. No evidence of congestive heart failure. The retinae showed moderate vascular sclerosis, discs normal; no hemorrhages or areas of degeneration. The urine was positive for protein and negative for blood. Concentrating capacity normal. No previous history of glomerulonephritis, pyelonephritis, or uropathology. Retrograde pyelograms were normal. Diagnosis: essential hypertension. On 10/18/40 with glucose titration, $C_M = 120$, $Tm_G = 410$ (load/T_G ratio = 1.73), B.P. = 138/92. On 10/23/40 with glucose titration repeated, $C_M = 138$, B.P. = 155/110. On 11/8/40 with glucose and diodrast titration, $C_D = 718$, $C_M = 130$, B.P. = 142/99. On 11/15/40 with diodrast titration, $C_M = 111$, $Tm_D = 43.3$ (load/T_D ratio = 2.6–4.7), B.P. = 152/110, $V_o/Tm_D = 14.5$, or 125 per cent of normal. $C_{IN}/Tm_G = 0.300$, or 81 per cent of normal.

This subject has a mean tubular perfusion rate 25 per cent above normal and a normal distribution of this perfusate, while the mean glomerular activity is only slightly below the normal (81 per cent); yet the distribution of glomerular activity is highly abnormal. A large number of glomeruli have an activity only 60 per cent of the mean, these being balanced by glomeruli having activities up to 80 per cent above the mean. Indeed, there are very few glomeruli with an activity equal to the mean.

In this instance, it must be supposed that localized arterial lesions have in effect divided the kidney into "affected" and "unaffected" glomeruli, while leaving tubular perfusion essentially undisturbed.

(It is possible that because of the low activity in some glomeruli, we had not reached definitive Tm_G even at a load/T_G ratio of 1.73; but if Tm_G is actually higher than our figure of 410, the effect on the titration and frequency distribution curves will be only to move the two modes away from the mean and to flatten the trough, *i.e.*, to exaggerate the present picture.)

125

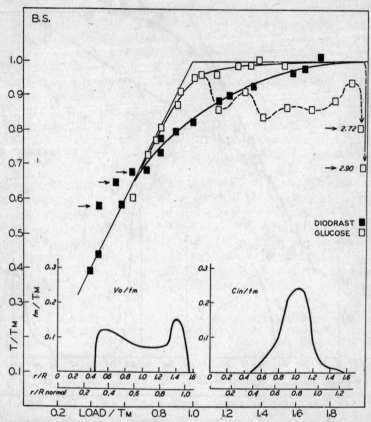

FIG. 12. B. S., 44 year old white female. Hypertension of relatively short duration. Blood pressure ranged from 210/100 to 140/68 mm. Hg, falling promptly on bed rest. Heart slightly enlarged and ECG normal. No evidence of congestive heart failure. The retinae showed no vascular changes and the discs were normal. Urine negative for protein and blood. Concentrating capacity normal. Clinical diagnosis: essential hypertension. No previous history suggesting glomerulonephritis, pyelonephritis or uropathology. There is no clinical evidence of widespread arteriolar disease. The fluctuating blood pressure, age of the patient and apparent short duration suggest the type of hypertension commonly seen in the climacteric. On 11/28/41, $C_D = 356$, $C_M = 101$, $Tm_D = 37.0$ (load/$T_D = 1.9$), B.P. = 186/100. On 12/10/41, $C_D = 357$, $C_M = 81$, B.P. = 162/88; during titration C_D increased to 426, from which figure V_o is calculated. Titration was repeated on 12/17/41, B.P. = 170/96, taking V_o as on 12/10/41; there was a transient hyperemia which lasted for 3 periods (arrows). (Also see below.) $V_o/Tm_D = 8.0$ or 67 per cent of normal. Some uncertainty is attached to the titration curve as influenced by V_o, but no acceptable reinterpretation would abolish a wide dispersion.

First glucose titration was carried out on 1/14/42 (B.P. = 172/90), the infusion consisting of glucose in saline, 2.5 to 6.0 cc. per minute, and the patient having had only 200 cc. of water on the morning of the test. After period 5, T_G began to fall, as shown by the dotted line, ending at a much reduced value. We believe that this fall in T_G represents glomerular occlusion in consequence of the development of renal edema and increased intrarenal pressure. Titration repeated on 1/23/42, duplicating the procedures of 1/14/42 except that the infusion was made up in distilled water. T_G rose regularly to average 217 in 4 periods at load/T_G ratios of 1.76 to 2.26, but after period 12 it began to fall, to end at 83 per cent of this value in period 15 at a load/T_G ratio of 2.72 ($P_G = 600$ mg. per cent). Glo-

pendent glomeruli. Such lesions would tend to divide the kidney into two categories, "affected glomeruli" and "unaffected glomeruli," and thus break the frequency distribution curve into hypoactive and hyperactive glomeruli, using these expressions, of course, relative to the mean.   It is conceivable that, consequent to such lesions, activity in the unaffected glomeruli might, by way of compensation, be increased, thus further separating the two categories in respect to activity.   Relative to the last point, r/R_{normal} in the more active category in those subjects who show bimodal curves is *ca.* 0.6 (S. W.), 0.85 (T. T.), 1.1 (A. C.), 1.5 (S. K.) and 1.5 (A. M.); *i.e.*, in only two subjects is the activity of the more active category substantially above the normal mean.   The question of compensatory increase in activity of "unaffected glomeruli" must be left to investigation.

The circumstance that even where arterial lesions have broken the pattern of glomerular activity into widely separated categories,[24] tubular perfusion may remain essentially unaffected is to be explained, we believe, on the basis that, first, the capillaries arising from the efferent arterioles undergo considerable anastomosis, so that blood from a normally "active" glomerulus may perfuse the tubule attached to a relatively "inactive" glomerulus; and secondly, as we have pointed out above, the circulation of interstitial fluid, coupled with simple diffusion, will tend to maintain uniformity of tubular perfusion in the face of

[24] Obviously, these two "widely separated" categories of glomeruli might be in the two separate kidneys. We have not attempted to apply the titration method to the two kidneys separately, and reiterate that at the moment we are discussing the method in principle and not in definitive application.

---

merular occlusion was apparently avoided on this occasion until the last 3 periods, and accordingly the maximal value, 217, is taken as Tm_G.

On both occasions the total filtration rate increased during the titration process, the rise amounting to an increase of 27 and 19 per cent above the initial value, indicating that an increase in glomerular activity occurred in other nephrons which more than compensated for the loss of the occluded units. C_D was followed throughout, and increased on both occasions *pari passu* with the filtration rate, maintaining a nearly constant filtration fraction (0.18–0.20).

Although both Tm_D (37.0) and Tm_G (217) are small, the ratio Tm_G/Tm_D (5.9) is in the lower range of normal, while the basal values of C_{IN}/Tm_G (0.330 to 0.400) range across the normal mean, and hence it appears that the total quantity of tubular tissue, both excretory and reabsorptive, is but little reduced. It is to be noted, however, that the relative tubular perfusion rate is the lowest of all subjects examined here (C_D/Tm_D = 9.65, or -2.08σ relative to normal standards). The filtration fraction as averaged from all observations is less than 20 per cent, a figure too low to permit this extreme ischemia to be explained on the basis of increased efferent tonus alone. The frequency distribution curve of tubular perfusion is exceptional in being flat and tending towards bimodality, suggesting gross impediment of large vascular areas. On the other hand, the frequency distribution curve of glomerular activity is also unique for hypertensive subjects, in that it is practically normal, indicating that there are no severe lesions in the arteriolar tree. This combination of circumstances suggests a clinically unrecognized disturbance in the kidney involving either renal edema (possibly of endocrine origin) or interstitial fibrosis, such that tubular perfusion is markedly impaired, although C_{IN} remains within the normal range, as judged either by surface area, Tm_D or Tm_G. Either suggestion is in line with the circumstance that this patient showed the greatest tendency to renal disturbance (edema and glomerular occlusion ?) in consequence of infusion of glucose-saline solutions, of any of the subjects whom we have examined.

The data on this subject are interesting in that they demonstrate that a low rate of tubular perfusion will suffice to support glucose reabsorption, otherwise the severe ischemia of some tubules would lead to an increased dispersion of c_{in}/tm.

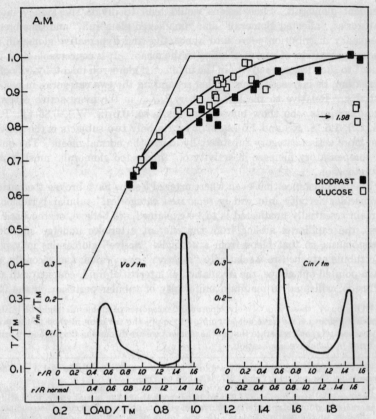

FIG. 13. A. M., 50 year old white female. Hypertension of relatively short duration.
Blood pressure ranged from 165/115 to 138/80 mm. Hg, falling promptly on bed rest. The
heart was not enlarged; the ECG showed low voltage and left deviation. No evidence of
congestive heart failure. Retinae showed no vascular changes; discs normal. The urine
was negative for protein and blood. Concentrating capacity normal. No previous history
of glomerulonephritis, pyelonephritis or uropathology. Intravenous pyelogram normal.
The patient showed the lethargy, skin changes, loss of hair and low voltage in the ECG
suggestive of myxedema. The BMR was within the normal range. Diagnosis: essential
hypertension. On 1/28/42 with diodrast titration, $C_D = 378$, $C_M = 65.4$, B.P. = 162/88.
On 2/2/42 with glucose titration, C_D increased during titration from 352 to 559, $C_M = 77.7$,
B.P. = 152/90. On 2/9/42 with glucose titration, $C_M = 89.4$, $Tm_G = 211$ (load/T_G ratio =
1.55–1.92), B.P. = 142/74, C_D remaining between 524 and 666 during titration. On 2/16/42
with diodrast titration, $C_D = 415$, $C_M = 70.6$, $Tm_D = 28.8$ (load/T_D ratio = 2.16–3.54),
B.P. = 140/82. On 2/23/42 with diodrast titration, $C_D = 399$, $C_M = 62.6$, B.P. = 132/80.
$V_o/Tm_D = 11.6$ or 98 per cent of normal. $C_{IN}/Tm_G = 0.422$ or 107 per cent of normal.
Here both tubular perfusion and glomerular activity are abnormal in being bimodal,
though the mean of both functions is somewhat above normal. On one occasion, T_G fell
in the latter part of glucose titration, and at a load/T_G ratio of 1.98, to 80 per cent of Tm_G,
indicating occlusion of glomeruli. This phenomenon was much more evident, however, in
B. S. (fig. 12). It must be inferred that in this patient renal lesions are such as to impair
the circulation to both glomeruli and tubules, though why tubular perfusion is impaired
here to a so much greater extent than in our other subjects is unexplained.

local arteriolar disease. Our present data argue against the belief that local
tubular ischemia is readily obtained.

It is worthy of note that where glomerular activity has a sharply abnormal pattern, while yet the mean is essentially normal, the abnormal pattern tends to consist of bimodal curve wherein those glomeruli of low activity are balanced by a large number of moderately active glomeruli, rather than by a diminishing series of glomeruli having progressively greater activity. Were the latter the case, relatively high values of glomerular activity would have to be reached in some nephrons and in consequence these nephrons would spill glucose at relatively low plasma glucose levels. The circumstance that hypertensive subjects do not typically show glycosuria suggests that the subjects we have examined are, in this respect, typical of the disease, rather than exceptions.

VIII. OCCLUSION OF GLOMERULI

One point requiring emphasis in closing, is the tendency of some subjects to show a marked decrease in T_G during the course of glucose titration or determination of Tm_G. This is particularly well illustrated by B. S. (fig. 12). This paradoxical fall in T_G has, in our experience, occurred only after some 90 to 150 minutes perfusion with saline-glucose solution mixtures containing mannitol but negligible quantities of diodrast at the rate of 4 to 6 cc. per minute. However, we have demonstrated that while maintaining a load/T_G ratio of 0.9 to 1.3, T_G may be substantially lowered by the more rapid (20 to 30 cc. per minute) infusion of 1000 cc. of saline.[25] We believe that it is the fluid rather than the glucose, mannitol or diodrast which is responsible. The explanation of this phenomenon is obscure, but we would suggest as a possible explanation that when fluid, and notably saline, is presented to the body too rapidly it tends to cause renal edema, and consequently to increase intrarenal pressure. This pressure could act to reduce the filtration rate in at least some glomeruli, particularly those in or near the *cortex corticus*, perhaps even to the point of complete occlusion. A fall to T_G of 20 to 30 per cent has been observed under these conditions (A. M., fig. 13, B. S., fig. 12), but it is not beyond possibility that nearly this fraction of glomeruli could be completely occluded, or the filtration rate so reduced in a complementary fraction as to effect this reduction in T_G. This explanation is tentative, and useful only until the phenomenon can be examined more thoroughly; but, if correct, it indicates that increased intrarenal pressure associated with intrarenal edema may play an important part in determining the frequency distribution of glomerular activity in disease.

Perhaps the most interesting part of this glomerular occlusion is the circumstance that it is generally accompanied by an increase in total filtration rate and in effective renal blood flow (see C_D data in figs. 10, 12, 13).[26] There is evidence that edema of peripheral tissues is frequently accompanied by hyperemia, and

[25] Partial glucose titration curves of normal subjects before, during and after saline administration were described at the Chicago meeting (1941) of the Federation of American Biological Societies.

[26] Space does not permit inclusion of the data, but the increase in effective renal blood flow is generally accompanied by a proportional increase in filtration rate, indicating afferent arteriolar dilatation. Shannon (30) has shown that saline infusion increases the filtration rate in the dog, and from the glomerular dynamics in this species it may be surmised that there is simultaneously renal hyperemia.

the above observations indicate that the kidney similarly responds to edema by hyperemia, effected by dilatation of still active glomeruli.

If the above interpretation is correct, it brings out the weakest point in the glucose titration method, viz., that the administration of large quantities of saline (plus glucose ?) is apt to distort the normal pattern of glomerular activity. We believe that we have excluded from the experiments presented here those in which this complication is serious, but the difficulties presented by this hazard, especially in hypertensive subjects, are considerable. We hope that before the titration method is extensively applied a substitute for glucose, which can be administered in small quantities and in small amounts of saline, can be made available so that the hazard may be wholly circumvented.

SUMMARY

1. A brief résumé of the problems presented by possible intermittency of glomerular activity and tubular perfusion is presented.

2. Data are given on the maximal rate of glucose reabsorption (Tm_G) in 24 men and 11 women without evidence of renal disease. Supplementary data are included on the filtration rate (C_{IN}), the diodrast clearance (C_D) and the maximal rate of tubular excretion of diodrast (Tm_D) in these same subjects in order to permit a comparison of these data with Tm_G.

Tm_G and Tm_D are not significantly modified by adrenalin, caffeine, or pyrogenic hyperemia, indicating the intrinsic stability both of the underlying tubular mechanisms of reabsorption and excretion, and of the glomerular and tubular blood supply. Since saturation of the glucose reabsorptive mechanism does not modify Tm_D, and vice versa, and since both tubular reabsorption (glucose) and tubular excretion (diodrast) are probably localized in the proximal tubule, it appears that independent chemical mechanisms may co-exist in the same tubule cell.

3. The statistical means in the present series of normal subjects in respect to C_{IN}, C_D and Tm_D are in good agreement with the data presented in a previous paper. The previous and present series have been combined to afford new statistical references, the data on the sexes being treated separately since they differ significantly.

Tm_G is positively correlated with C_{IN}, suggesting a developmental relationship between the rate of filtration in a particular nephron and the reabsorptive capacity of the attached tubule. Tm_G is poorly correlated with Tm_D, showing that the reabsorptive and excretory capacities of the tubule may be developed quite differently in the same individual, and presumably in the same nephron.

4. Data on Tm_G and other functional measurements are presented on subjects with essential hypertension. In these subjects Tm_G tends to remain within normal limits, being reduced only after a marked reduction in Tm_D has occurred; and the ratio C_{IN}/Tm_G adheres closely to the normal ratio, indicating that glucose reabsorption is not specifically impaired in hypertensive disease, Tm_G being reduced only after the glomerulus of a nephron is obliterated by vascular changes and the tubule thereby cut off passively from reabsorptive activity.

The reduction in Tm_D is the earliest characteristic impairment in renal function so far observed in hypertensive disease. If tubular excretion represents a final step in a series of metabolic reactions in the kidney, this impairment may have special significance.

5. It is assumed that the maximal rates of reabsorption of glucose (Tm_G) and excretion of diodrast (Tm_D) which characterize the over-all activity of the two kidneys, reflect similar quantitative limitations in each nephron. Under this assumption, the titration of the kidneys by the progressive elevation of the glucose or diodrast concentration in the plasma affords a means of measuring glomerular activity and tubular perfusion in component portions of the kidneys.

Glomerular activity is defined as the rate of glomerular filtration in cc. per minute per unit of glucose reabsorptive tissue in the attached nephron; while tubular perfusion is defined as the rate of flow in cc. per minute per unit of tubular excretory tissue of a fluid having the same concentration of diodrast as the post-glomerular plasma.

These titration methods have been developed in a quantitative manner and applied to the determination of the dispersion of glomerular activity and tubular perfusion in normal and hypertensive subjects.

6. In normal subjects no appreciable number of nephrons have a glomerular activity below 0.60 or above 1.5 times the mean glomerular activity for the entire kidneys; the glomerular activity being distributed about the mean in a manner roughly conforming with a normal frequency distribution curve, the dispersion of which is such that 95 per cent of the nephrons fall within ±40 per cent of the mean. That is to say, there is no large number of nephrons (*i.e.*, the fraction is no greater than 5 per cent) in which glomerular activity is less than 60 per cent of the mean; hence the notion of "glomerular reserve" posited on an assumption of glomerular intermittency carried over from cold-blooded vertebrates, is untenable.

In normal subjects no appreciable quantity of tubular tissue has a perfusion rate below 0.66 or above 1.66 times the mean tubular perfusion for the entire kidneys; the relative perfusion rate is distributed about the mean in a manner roughly conforming with a normal frequency distribution curve, the dispersion of which is such that 95 per cent of the tubular tissue is perfused at a rate within ±40 per cent of the mean.

7. By way of example, rather than as a definitive study of the disease, the data obtained by the application of the titration methods to seven subjects with essential hypertension are given in detail. Several notable features emerge from this study:

The distribution of tubular perfusate and glomerular activity may be entirely normal despite long-standing hypertension.

There is an evident tendency for tubular perfusion to persist within the normal range and to maintain a normal pattern, in subjects in whom glomerular activity deviates from the normal pattern by separation into extremes of hypoactive and hyperactive glomeruli (both terms being used here relative to the subject's own mean of glomerular activity, and not the normal mean, which is infrequently exceeded). This result is interpreted as indicating that arterial lesions may affect large numbers of glomeruli adversely, while anastomoses of the post-glomerular capillaries and the circulation of interstitial fluid operate to maintain uniformity of tubular perfusion. It seems apparent that focal tubular ischemia will prove to be the exception, rather than the rule, in the hypertensive kidney.

8. The administration of saline may reduce Tm_G—a phenomenon tentatively attributed to the production of renal edema and increased intrarenal pressure. There is usually a simultaneous increase in the total filtration rate and effective renal blood flow, indicating that renal edema (if this is the correct explanation) is accompanied by hyperemia, as is the frequent case in other tissues.

The analysts in this work have been Katherine S. Tilson, Betty J. Crawford, Frances E. Marx, Martha J. Barrett and Helen Claire Lawler. We are indebted to them, and to nurses Helen R. McGuire, Ann S. Rivoire and Agatha A. Evaskitis for their unfailing co-operation.

The clearance technique and analytical methods used in this study were identical with those described in a previous paper (19) except for the substitution of Alpert's (3) iodine method, allowing 94 per cent recovery of diodrast in a 1:15 $CdSO_4$ filtrate, and Shannon's (31) glucose method. The inulin was ampouled material obtained from the U. S. Standard Products Company, Madison, Wisconsin, and the diodrast from the Winthrop Chemical Company, New York. Saline and glucose solutions (50 per cent) were prepared by Schering & Glatz, Inc., New York, to whom we are indebted for several lots of specially prepared glucose solution. The mannitol was supplied by courtesy by Sharp and Dohme, Philadelphia.

We are particularly indebted to Dr. H. M. C. Luykx for his valuable mathematical criticism and for his help in relating the titration to the frequency distribution curve.

Erratum

Two subordinate equations, used in the calculation of the ellipse in Figures 1 to 4 inclusive, contain typographical errors as given in our previous paper ((20) p. 638) and should read:

$$x = \frac{-ay}{2} \pm \sqrt{\left(\frac{a^2}{4} - b\right) y^2 - c}$$

$$c = -(1 - r^2)\chi^2\sigma^2$$

BIBLIOGRAPHY

1. ABRAMSON, D. I., AND SIDNEY, M. F.: Relationship between edema and rate of peripheral blood flow. J. Clin. Investigation, 21: 626, 1942.
2. ADOLPH, E. F.: Control of urine formation in the frog by the renal circulation. Am. J. Physiol., 117: 366, 1936.
3. ALPERT, L. K.: A rapid method for the determination of diodrast-iodine in blood and urine. Bull. Johns Hopkins Hosp., 68: 522, 1941.
4. BIETER, R. N.: The effect of the splanchnics upon glomerular blood flow in the frog's kidney. Am. J. Physiol., 91: 436, 1929.
5. Bradley, S. E., and Bing, R. J.: Renal function in the harbor seal (*Phoca vitulina L.*) during asphyxial ischemia and pyrogenic hyperemia. J. Cell. & Comp. Physiol., 19: 229, 1942.
6. CHASIS, H., AND REDISH, J.: Effective renal blood flow in the separate kidneys of subjects with essential hypertension. J. Clin. Investigation, 20: 655, 1941
7. CHASIS, H., RANGES, H. A., GOLDRING, W., AND SMITH, H. W.: The control of renal blood flow and glomerular filtration in normal man. J. Clin. Investigation, 17: 683, 1938.

8. CHESLEY, L. C., CONNELL, E. J., CHESLEY, E. R., KATZ, J. D., AND GLISSEN, C. S.: The diodrast clearance and renal blood flow in toxemias of pregnancy. J. Clin. Investigation, 19: 219, 1940.

9. CLARKE, R. W.: The xylose clearance of *myoxocephalus octodecimspinosus* under normal and diuretic conditions. J. Cell. & Comp. Physiol., 5: 73, 1934.

10. CORCORAN, A. C., AND PAGE, I. H.: Renal blood flow in experimental renal hypertension. Am. J. Physiol., 135: 361, 1941.

11. CORCORAN, A. C., SMITH, H. W., AND PAGE; I. H.: The removal of diodrast from blood by the dog's explanted kidney. Am. J. Physiol., 134: 333, 1941.

12. EKEHORN, G.: On the principles of renal function. Acta med. Scandinav., 74: Sup. 36, 1931.

13. FINKELSTEIN, N., ALIMINOSA, L. M., AND SMITH, H. W.: The renal clearances of hippuric acid and pyridone derivatives. Am. J. Physiol., 133: P. 276, 1941.

14. FOA, P. P., WOODS, W. W., PEET, M. M., AND FOA, N. L.: Studies relative to the physiological basis of splanchnicectomy in the treatment of hypertension. Univ. Hosp. Bull., Ann Arbor, 8: 9, 1942.

15. FORSTER, R. P.: The use of inulin and creatinine as glomerular filtrate measuring substances in the frog. J. Cell. & Comp. Physiol., 12: 213, 1938.

16. FORSTER, R. P.: The nature of the glucose reabsorptive process in the frog renal tubule. Evidence for intermittency of glomerular function in the intact animal. J. Cell. & Comp. Physiol., 20: 55, 1942.

17. FRIEDMAN, M., SELZER, A., KREUTZMANN, H., AND SAMPSON, J. J.: The changes in the blood pressure and in the renal blood flow and glomerular filtration rate of hypertensive patients following unilateral nephrectomy. J. Clin. Investigation, 21: 19, 1942.

18. FRIEDMAN, M., SUGARMAN, H., AND SELZER, A.: The relationship of renal blood pressure and blood flow to the production of experimental hypertension. Am. J. Physiol., 134: 493, 1941.

19. GOLDRING, W., CHASIS, H., RANGES, H. A., AND SMITH, H. W.: Relations of effective renal blood flow and glomerular filtration to tubular excretory mass in normal man. J. Clin. Investigation, 19: 739, 1940.

20. GOLDRING, W., CHASIS, H., RANGES, H. A., AND SMITH, H. W.: Effective renal blood flow in subjects with essential hypertension. J. Clin. Investigation, 20: 637, 1941.

21. HAYMAN, J. M., JR., AND STARR, I., JR.: Experiments on the glomerular distribution of blood in the mammalian kidney. J. Exper. Med., 42: 641, 1925.

22. HIATT, E. P., AND HIATT, R. B.: The effect of food on the glomerular filtration rate and renal blood flow in the harbor seal (*Phoca vitulina L.*). J. Cell. & Comp. Physiol., 19: 221, 1942.

23. KHANOLKAR, V. R.: Partial activity of the kidney and the "all or nothing" principle. J. Path. & Bact., 25: 414, 1922.

24. OLIVER, J.: Architecture of the kidney in chronic Bright's disease. New York, Paul Hoeber, 1939.

25. PEARL, R.: Introduction to medical biometry and statistics. Philadelphia, W. B. Saunders Co., 1940.

26. RANGES, H. A., CHASIS, H., GOLDRING, W., AND SMITH, H. W.: The functional measurement of the number of active glomeruli and tubules in the kidneys of normal and hypertensive subjects. Am. J. Physiol., 126: 603, 1939.

27. RICHARDS, A. N., BARNWELL, J. B., AND BRADLEY, R. C.: The effect of small amounts of adrenalin upon the glomerular blood vessels of the frog's kidney perfused at constant rate. Am. J. Physiol., 79: 410, 1927.

28. RICHARDS, A. N., AND SCHMIDT, C. F.: A description of the glomerular circulation in the frog's kidney and observations concerning the action of adrenalin and various other substances upon it. Am. J. Physiol., 71: 178, 1924–25.

29. SHANNON, J. A.: The tubular reabsorption of xylose in the normal dog. Am. J. Physiol., 122: 775, 1938.

30. SHANNON, J. A.: The control of the renal excretion of water. I. The effect of variations in the state of hydration on water excretion in dogs with diabetes insipidus. J. Exp. Med., 76: 371, 1942.

31. SHANNON, J. A., FARBER, S., AND TROAST, L.: The measurement of glucose Tm in the normal dog. Am. J. Physiol., 133: 752, 1941.

32. SHANNON, J. A., AND FISHER, S.: The renal tubular reabsorption of glucose in the normal dog. Am. J. Physiol., 122: 765, 1938.

33. SMITH, H. W.: The physiology of the kidney. Oxford Univ. Press, 1937.

34. SMITH, H. W.: The physiology of the renal circulation. Harvey Lectures, 35: 166, 1939–40.

35. SMITH, H. W.: Note on the interpretations of clearance methods in the diseased kidney. J. Clin. Investigation, 20: 631, 1941.

36. SMITH, H. W.: Is essential hypertension of renal origin? Bull. New York Acad. Med., in press.

37. SMITH, H. W., GOLDRING, W., AND CHASIS, H.: The measurement of the tubular excretory mass, effective blood flow and filtration rate in the normal human kidney. J. Clin. Investigation, 17: 263, 1938.

38. SMITH, W. W., AND SMITH, H. W.: Protein binding of phenol red, diodrast, and other substances in plasma. J. Biol. Chem., 124: 107, 1938.

39. SPRINGORUM, P. W.: Zur frage der funktionellen bedeutung der arteriovenösen anastomosen für die niere. Klin. Wchnschr., 18: 811, 1939.

40. STEINITZ, K.: Zur frage der nierendurchblutung bei normalen, hypertonikern und nierenkranken. Acta Med. Scandinav., 109: 95, 1941.

41. WALKER, A. M., AND BOTT, P. A.; OLIVER, J., AND MACDOWELL, M. C.: The collection and analysis of fluid from single nephrons of the mammalian kidney. Am. J. Physiol., 134: 580, 1941.

42. WELLEN, I., WELSH, C. A., AND TAYLOR, H. C., JR.: The filtration rate, effective renal blood flow, tubular excretory mass and phenol red clearance in specific toxemia of pregnancy. J. Clin. Investigation, 21: 63, 1942.

43. WELSH, C. A., ROSENTHAL, A., DUNCAN, M. T., AND TAYLOR, H. C., JR.: The effects of testosterone propionate on renal function in the dog, as measured by the creatinine and diodrast clearance and diodrast Tm. Am. J. Physiol., 137: 338, 1942.

44. WHITE, H. L.: Observations on the nature of glomerular activity. Am. J. Physiol., 90: 689, 1929.

45. WHITE, H. L.: Observations indicating absence of glomerular intermittence in normal dogs and rabbits. Am. J. Physiol., 128: 159, 1939.

46. WHITE, H. L.: Observations on the behavior of diodrast in the dog. Am. J. Physiol., 130: 454, 1940.

47. WHITE, H. L., Heinbecker, P., AND Rolf, D.: Effects of the removal of the anterior lobe of the hypophysis on some renal functions. Am. J. Physiol., 137: 584, 1942.